HARPS & HOODS

Ice-breeding seals of the Northwest Atlantic

HARPS & HOODS

Ice-breeding seals of the Northwest Atlantic

David M. Lavigne and Kit M. Kovacs

University of Waterloo Press

ISBN 0-88898-081-7

University of Waterloo Press
Dana Porter Library
University of Waterloo
Waterloo, Ontario, Canada
N2L 3G1

Design: Dave Bartholomew, Graphic Services, University of Waterloo.

Printed in Canada

Canadian Cataloguing in Publication Data

Lavigne, D.M. (David Martin), 1946-
    Harps & Hoods: Ice-breeding seals of the Northwest Atlantic

Bibliography: p.
Includes index.
ISBN 0-88898-081-7

1. Harp seal. 2. Hooded seal. 3. Sealing – Atlantic Ocean. I. Kovacs, Kit M. 1956- II. Title.

QL737.P64L38 1988   599.74'8   C87-094650-1

Contents

Foreword ix
Preface xi
Acknowledgements xv

1. **Introduction** 1
   The harp seal 6
   The hooded seal 8

2. **Distribution and Migration** 11
   Harp seals 11
   Hooded seals 16

3. **Life Cycles** 21
   Harp seals 21
   Hooded seals 45

4. **Adaptations for Life in the Sea** 55
   Thermoregulation 58
   Locomotion 64
   Diving 67
   Senses 78
       Vision 78
       Hearing 84
       Echolocation 86
       Vibrissae 87
       Smell 88
   Feeding adaptations 88
   Water balance 91
   Reproductive strategies 92

5. **History of the Northwest Atlantic Seal Hunt** 99
   The first European sealers 100
   The beginnings of the Newfoundland seal hunt 104
   Early sealing in the Magdalen Islands 107
   The Golden Age of Sealing, 1818-1862 112
   The wooded-walled steamers, 1863-1943 115
   Steel-hulled steamers 121
   Post-war sealing 129
   Years of controversy, 1964 – 132

6. **Future Prospects** 151

Selected readings 159
Tourist information 163
Glossary 165
Index 169
The Authors 172

These two especial types of Hair Seals have been known colloquially from time immemorial to all in Newfoundland – as the "Harps" and the "Hoods" – these descriptive names having been given to them from certain respective characteristics which appealed, from their shape and oddity, to the imagination of the Island's fishermen and sealers of the earliest days. Since then, and for over a century and a half of pursuit, the Harps and the Hoods have been held famous; and it is the adventure of their capture on the great western Floes carried south by the Labrador current in every Spring, that has brought both wealth and romance to the Dominion of Terra Nova.

Major William Howe Greene, O.B.E., F.R.I.B.A.

The Wooden Walls Among the Ice Floes,
Telling the Romance of the Newfoundland Seal Fishery (1933)

Foreword

The following pages graphically portray the Canadian harp and hooded seals and their fight for survival ... against both nature and man. It is an epic struggle spanning the centuries.

These beautiful animals are ... as the authors demonstrate so well ... superbly equipped to meet nature on equal terms. They have, however, few defences against human enemies.

I fell under the spell of the harp seals on my very first visit to their ice nurseries in the Gulf of St. Lawrence – March 12, 1965. It was then that I dedicated my life to protecting the seals. To me, they are perhaps the loveliest creatures on Earth.

Even then, it occurred to me that the harp seal nursery in the Gulf of St. Lawrence offered a tourist attraction of unparalleled beauty.

In March 1970, I took twelve tourists to see the seals. Enthralled humans photographed baby harp seals and watched in fascination as adults moved like quicksilver across the blue water in open leads. The only sound of their passing was the water lapping against the glittering ice.

Today, one question is being increasingly and hopefully asked. Can tourism to the seal herd ever be an economically viable industry?

I believe it can. With the demise of the seal hunt in recent years and changing attitudes within the Canadian Department of Fisheries and Oceans, the opportunity is ripe.

Tourists have returned to the ice and The International Fund for Animal Welfare is striving to make my dream of nearly twenty years a reality. I want to make the seals' annual visit to the Gulf a peaceful spectacle that can be enjoyed by people from all over the world.

It is my hope that many of you, having read the pages that follow, will join me on the ice one March as IFAW continues its annual *'Seal Watch'.* It is a unique opportunity to participate in one of the most spectacular wildlife adventures in North America.

Brian D. Davies
Founder, International Fund for Animal Welfare

Preface

At first, it seemed like a relatively easy undertaking: produce a 'little booklet' – essentially a field guide – for the use of tourists who now go seal watching in the the Gulf of St. Lawrence each spring. As originally conceived, the booklet would describe in words and pictures what tourists might expect to see on a typical visit to the ice and to place this into the larger context of the seals' life story. It would also attempt to answer the questions most frequently asked by tourists, both before and after their visits to the ice.

Before we really got started, we realized that such a booklet might, with some rethinking, serve other purposes as well. Each spring, biologists who work on harp seals are inundated with questions from students, teachers, naturalists, environmental groups, animal welfare organizations, the general public and the media about the biology and management of harp seals and about the controversy surrounding the annual seal hunt. Although much has been written on these subjects in recent decades, there is still no single and widely accessible source of information to which interested persons can refer. As a result, the project began to grow and in the process, our 'little booklet' evolved into this small book.

The book tells the story of two kinds of seals. One of these is the well known harp seal. It produces its photogenic white-coated offspring on pack ice off the east coast of Canada each February and March. The other is the hooded seal. Although vastly outnumbered and overshadowed by the harp seal, it too appears on the ice for its own annual breeding ritual. It is during this spring breeding season that for centuries both species have been slaughtered for their blubber or their pelts.

Chapter 1 introduces the harps and hoods and describes their relationship with other seals, sea lions, fur seals and the walrus. Although the book deals primarily with harp and hooded seals in the northwest Atlantic off eastern Canada, both species are more widely distributed than this and both undertake extensive migrations each year. The various populations of harp and hooded seals and their annual migrations are outlined in Chapter 2.

When tourists visit the ice for a few hours in March they see only a brief snapshot in the life of the seals. Those who visit early in March see a very different picture than do those who arrive a week or two later. In Chapter 3, we describe in some detail the life cycles of harp and hooded seals, concentrating especially on the rapidly changing series of events that occur within a few weeks during the spring breeding season. Hopefully, with the aid of the photographs, tourists will be able to place their visits into better context and other readers will gain a greater appreciation of the natural history of the two species.

Humans have long been fascinated by marine mammals, especially seals and whales. Encounters with seals invariably generate a long list of questions about how they manage to do the things they do: How do they stay under water for so long? How do they find their food? Do they get the 'bends'? Etc., etc. These sorts of questions are addressed in Chapter 4.

The current awareness of harp and hooded seals has been generated by the on-going controversy that has surrounded the seal hunt off eastern Canada for more than two decades. To put this controversy into perspective requires an appreciation of the history of the seal hunt. It is a long and often tragic history. In Chapter 5, we provide only an overview. No attempt is made to give a detailed analysis of the seal-hunt controversy or the politics of sealing – that will have to await the writing of a much longer book.

Despite claims in the press that the Canadian seal hunt has ended, it has not. As we approach the end of the 20th century, the story of seals and sealing in Canada continues to unfold. In the concluding chapter, we attempt to answer some of the most frequently asked questions about the present status of the seal herds. We also deal with the concerns about the seals' perceived interactions with commercial fisheries, should the smaller hunts of the last few years continue into the 1990s and beyond.

We have written this book for a wide audience composed of what academics typically describe as 'well informed lay persons'. Such a group might span the range from high school students writing essays or term papers about seals or the seal hunt, to professional colleagues who, although interested in the topic, have no special knowledge of seals and sealing. Such an audience does not usually want to be overwhelmed by long lists of hard-to-find documents or detailed footnotes that characterize more technical publications. Therefore, at the risk of frustrating the more serious students, we have not included references in the text, nor have we provided an extensive bibliography of the sources we consulted while writing the book. Instead, we have provided a list of selected readings for each chapter. These readings and the bibliographies they contain should direct interested readers to additional material so that they can pursue their own specific interests in more detail or from different perspectives.

We have tried to minimize the use of unnecessary technical terms and scientific jargon that so often makes the writings of academics virtually inaccessible to a wide audience. Where technical language was unavoidable, we have provided a definition of the term either in the text or in a Glossary at the end of the book. All terms in the Glossary are printed in **bold** the first time they appear.

One final comment. Words and pictures cannot adequately describe what it is like to stand on a frozen ocean, a vast white and windswept moonscape, surrounded by hundreds of harp seals and their pups or beside a 'family' of hooded seals. Some days it can be extremely cold; others are bright, sunny and warm – if you call 0°C or 32°F warm! Regardless of the conditions, it is always an incredible experience. If you ever have the inclination and the opportunity to see the seals for yourself, do not hesitate. It is a trip well worth the taking.

D.M.L. & K.M.K.

October 1987
Rockwood, ON

Acknowledgements

We express our sincere gratitude to those biologists and writers, past and present, who provided the raw material upon which this book is based. Although most of these individuals remain anonymous in a book of this sort, the final product would have been very different without their individual contributions.

We also thank those who reviewed earlier drafts of individual chapters or the entire manuscript and who made numerous suggestions for its improvement. They include Brian Davies, Lin Downes, Charles Genore, Dr. Stuart Innes, Jean Kinloch, Dr. Murray Kinloch, Pauline Lavigne, Sara Lavigne, Richard Moore, Dr. Tom Nudds, Dr. Christopher Nunan, Annemieke Roell, Ann Smith, Gloria Smith and Dr. Vernon Thomas. We must admit, however, that we did not always take the advice of our reviewers and obviously we are responsible for any errors that remain.

The contribution of Murray Kinloch, Professor of English, University of New Brunswick, deserves special thanks. Not only did he provide extensive comments on the initial draft and point out several things our grammar teachers failed to teach us, he also proof-read the final manuscript before our diskettes were submitted for type-setting.

A number of colleagues generously gave us access to their slide collections to supplement our illustrations in the text. For their willing assistance, we thank Ron Brooks, Dan Costa, Robert Frank, John Hickie, Stuart Innes, Norman Lightfoot, Ted Miller, Keith Ronald and Rob Stewart. We also thank John Kaprielian, Photo Researchers Inc., New York, NY, for his help in securing a particularly elusive image.

Pictures from the past were provided by the Provin-

Pictures from the past were provided by the Provincial Archives of Newfoundland & Labrador, St. John's, Newfoundland. We particularly thank Tony Murphy, Archives Technician (Still & Moving Images), for his efforts on our behalf. Additional photos were obtained from the slide library of the International Fund for Animal Welfare.

We sincerely thank David Blackwood for allowing us to reproduce one of his powerful images – S. S. *Imogene* – *Leaving for the Icefields* – to lead off Chapter 5. David's art uniquely captures the human element in the story of the *Harps & Hoods* in the late 19th and early 20th centuries and we are delighted to be able to include an example of it in our book.

We also thank Gloria Smith, University of Waterloo Press, Dave Bartholomew, Graphic Services, University of Waterloo and Bruce Uttley, Computing Services, University of Waterloo, for their interest in the project, for their guidance and for turning our manuscript, slides and photographs into a book.

This book is a natural outgrowth of our research on the biology of harp and hooded seals. The research would not have been undertaken without the generous support, over the last 15 years, of a number of government agencies and a variety of groups and organizations. These include: The Natural Sciences and Engineering Research Council of Canada; The Department of Fisheries and Oceans and the Department of Supply and Services, Government of Canada; World Wildlife Fund (Canada); The Donner Canadian Foundation and The Canadian National Sportsmens' Show Fund; Greenpeace and the International Fund for Animal Welfare (IFAW).

The inclusion of Greenpeace and IFAW in this list may surprise some readers. There is a view, expressed by Guy Wright, in his book, *Sons & Seals, A Voyage to the Ice* (Institute of Social and Economic Research, Memorial University of Newfoundland, St. John's, Newfoundland, 1984, p. 23), that 'none of the [anti-sealing] groups have undertaken or sponsored any scientific studies....' Wright and others holding this view are wrong. Numerous animal welfare and environmental groups frequently undertake or sponsor scientific studies to address specific problems or questions. And in our experience, these groups, like the other funding agencies we have dealt with, have invariably provided their financial support with no strings attached.

Finally, we owe a special thanks to Richard Moore, Executive Director, International Fund for Animal Welfare. He enthusiastically embraced our proposal to undertake this project and provided the necessary financial backing to La Vie Wildlife Research Associates Ltd., Rockwood, Ontario, to allow us to research and produce the book. We sincerely thank Richard, and IFAW's Founder, Brian Davies, for giving us the opportunity to write *our* book.

In his recent autobiography, *Metamorphosis* (1987, Stoddart Publishing Co. Limited), Dr. David Suzuki wrote:

> There is no such thing as objective reality. We select our experiences through the filters of our genes, values and belief systems.

While we are satisfied that the book accurately reflects our filtered experiences, we also accept that it may not always mirror the perceptions of others, including the individuals and organizations named above.

The pinnipeds.

TOP: Family Otariidae, Antarctic fur seal. *Photo: D. Costa*

MIDDLE: Family Odobenidae, walrus. *Photo: E.H. Miller*

BOTTOM: Family Phocidae, harbour seal.

1. Introduction

We are flying in a two-toned world: blue sky above, white, snow-covered ice below. Dressed in parkas, the four of us and our research equipment fill the helicopter. The noise inside is deafening and, without head-sets, attempts at conversation are futile. Distance is measured not in kilometers or miles but in minutes of flying time. In a headwind, time seems to stand still. For an hour we fly out of Charlottetown, Prince Edward Island. The scene below remains a monotonous white, broken occasionally by black **leads** of open water coursing through the ice. Suddenly, a finger in the front seat points out of the window. Eyes search and strain, and finally, there they are – seals.

Harp seals from the helicopter.

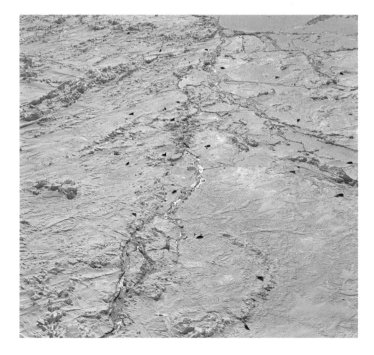

We circle to land and we are relieved when the engine is finally stilled. We wait for the rotor-blades to make their last revolution before opening the door. A frigid gust of wind greets us as we step carefully onto the pontoon and then, tentatively, down to the ice. Adult seals slither away from us.

'Chopper' on the ice.
Photo: N. Lightfoot

After the din of the helicopter, the silence is striking, broken only by the wind and the plaintive cries of white-coated seal pups. Today we will spend ten hours on the ice studying various aspects of harp seal biology, a routine we will repeat every day, weather permitting, for the next five weeks. Toward the end of our stay, we will encounter a second species that breeds on the ice – the hooded seal.

Harp and hooded seals belong to a group of mammals known as **pinnipeds** (meaning feather-, fin- or web-footed). There are 33 living species of pinnipeds; a 34th, the Caribbean monk seal, has not been seen since the 1950s and is presumed extinct. A complete list of the modern pinnipeds is provided in the accompanying table.

Pinnipeds are relatively large mammals, ranging in size from small female fur seals weighing less than 50 kilograms (110 pounds) to massive adult male southern elephant seals that may weigh as much as 3,600 kilograms (almost four tons). In many species, the males are considerably larger than the females, but in some, the sexes are of equal size or females are the larger sex. The bodies of pinnipeds are streamlined and, as their name suggests, their limbs are modified as flippers.

The modern pinnipeds

	Species	Common Name
Walrus	*Odobenus rosmarus*	walrus
Fur seals	*Callorhinus ursinus*	northern fur seal
	Arctocephalus townsendi	Guadalupe fur seal
	Arctocephalus philippii	Juan Fernandez fur seal
	Arctocephalus galapagoensis	Galapagos fur seal
	Arctocephalus australis	South American fur seal
	Arctocephalus pusillus	Cape (South African, Tasmanian, Australian, Victoria) fur seal
	Arctocephalus forsteri	New Zealand (Western Australian) fur seal
	Arctocephalus gazella	Antarctic (Kerguelen) fur seal
	Arctocephalus tropicalis	Subantarctic (Amsterdam Island) fur seal
Sea lions	*Eumetopias jubatus*	Steller (northern) sea lion
	Zalophus californianus	California sea lion
	Otaria byronia (= *O. flavescens*)	South American sea lion
	Neophoca cinerea	Australian sea lion
	Phocarctos hookeri	New Zealand sea lion

True seals

Monk seals

	Monachus monachus	Mediterranean monk seal
	Monachus tropicalis	Caribbean (West Indian) monk seal[1]
	Monachus schauinslandi	Hawaiian monk seal

Elephant seals

	Mirounga leonina	southern elephant seal
	Mirounga angustirostris	northern elephant seal

Antarctic seals

	Lobodon carcinophagus	crabeater seal
	Ommatophoca rossii	Ross seal
	Hydrurga leptonyx	leopard seal
	Leptonychotes weddellii	Weddell seal

Northern true seals

	Phoca vitulina	harbour (common) seal
	Phoca largha	largha (spotted) seal
	Pusa (= *Phoca*) *hispida*	ringed seal
	Pusa (= *Phoca*) *sibirica*	Baikal seal
	Pusa (= *Phoca*) *caspica*	Caspian seal
	Histriophoca (= *Phoca*) *fasciata*	ribbon seal
	Halichoerus grypus	grey seal
	Erignathus barbatus	bearded seal
	Pagophilus (= *Phoca*) *groenlandicus*	harp seal
	Cystophora cristata	hooded seal

[1] presumed extinct.

Modern pinnipeds may be divided into three groups (biologists call them Families), largely on the basis of their physical appearance – the fur seals and sea lions (Family Otariidae); the walrus (Family Odobenidae); and the true seals (Family Phocidae).

The true seals may be further subdivided, on the basis of their appearance and where they are found, into monk seals, elephant seals, Antarctic seals and northern true seals. The latter group includes the harp and hooded seals.

True seals may be easily distinguished from other pinnipeds because their hind flippers extend behind the body and cannot be brought forward in order to walk. For this reason, Joel Allen, who wrote a classic book on North American pinnipeds in 1880, referred to them as 'wrigglers', an apt description of their movements on land or ice. The wrigglers also lack external ears and for this reason they are sometimes called 'earless seals'. The openings to the internal ears may be seen as small holes just behind the eyes.

An 'earless' seal – female grey seal.

In contrast, the fur seals and sea lions, which are frequently seen balancing balls on their noses in circuses, marine parks and aquaria, are able to bring their hind flippers underneath the body into order to walk or run, somewhat awkwardly, on land. Allen called these pinnipeds 'walkers'. The walkers have a small external ear, a flap of skin supported by cartilage, seen behind the eye, near the opening to the internal ear. For this reason they are often called 'eared seals'.

An 'eared' seal – male
Galapagos fur seal.
Photo: R.J. Brooks

The walrus is a peculiar pinniped that exhibits a curious combination of traits, some of which are typical of true seals while others are reminiscent of those of eared seals. Like true seals, the walruses lack an external ear but, like fur seals and sea lions, they can bring their hind flippers forward underneath their bodies. Nonetheless, the hind limbs of the walrus do not support the animal's weight so the walrus is more awkward at walking than are fur seals and sea lions.

Unlike the other pinnipeds, whose bodies are covered with hair, the walrus is virtually naked, its coat being reduced to scattered hairs over the surface of the body and to an impressive moustache. Male and female walruses are also the only pinnipeds whose canine teeth are greatly enlarged as tusks.

The pinnipeds evolved from a terrestrial ancestor related to modern dogs, bears, weasels and raccoons, members of a larger group of mammals that biologists refer to as the Order Carnivora. The fossil record indicates that the pinnipeds apparently separated from land mammals more than 23 million years ago in what is today the Pacific Ocean, probably in the region of California. From there, over millions of years, they dispersed throughout the North Pacific, into the Atlantic via the Central American Seaway – an ancient waterway that separated North and South America on several occasions over the last 20 million years – and later into the southern hemisphere.

An 'earless' walrus.

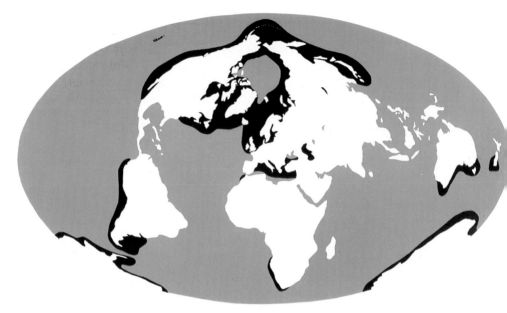

Global distribution of modern pinnipeds.

Today, pinnipeds occur mainly in the polar and subpolar regions of both the northern and southern hemispheres. Most are restricted to areas where the water is not only relatively cold (about 20°C or 68°F in the warmest month of the year) but also where there is a rich diversity of plant and animal life. Such productive regions provide an abundant supply of food for pinnipeds and other large marine animals.

With this very brief introduction to the pinnipeds, we will now look more closely at the harp and hooded seals. These two species have long been the subject of human concerns, first as a source of oil and leather and later because of their hair coats. Wider interests were aroused by the controversy surrounding the annual seal hunt. Today, the attraction of harps and hoods has taken on a new dimension: their breeding grounds offer a fascinating and unique experience for adventuresome tourists.

The harp seal

The harp seal is one of the more abundant and best known of all seal species and one dogged by controversy. Scientists cannot even reach unanimous agreement on its formal Latin name. Today, it is most commonly referred to as *Phoca groenlandica* (the Greenland seal) although some authors still use the more descriptive and poetic name, *Pagophilus groenlandicus* (the ice-lover from Greenland).

The harp seals' common name comes from the black, wish-bone shaped marking found on the backs of adult animals that someone, in the long-forgotten past, thought looked like a harp, the musical instrument most frequently associated with angels. Another name for this species, the saddle-backed seal, presumably arose as another interpretation of the appearance of this marking. The face is also black, in marked contrast to the remainder of the body which is silvery-grey.

Adult harp seal.

Adult male and female harp seals are the same size. On average, they are 169 centimeters (five and a half feet) long, and weigh about 130 kilograms (286 pounds), although their weight varies considerably throughout the year and from one year to the next.

Adult male hooded seal.

The hooded seal

The hooded seal is less numerous and less well known than the harp seal. Formerly known as the crested or bladder-nosed seal, the hooded seal gets both its scientific name, *Cystophora cristata* (*Cystophora* = bladder-carrying, *cristata* = crested) and its common names from the inflatable sac located on top of the nose and forehead of males.

Male hooded seals also have the unique and rather peculiar ability to fill the membrane between their nostrils with air, forming a large, red balloon that emerges through the left nostril. Both the hood and the inflated nasal septum are usually seen when male hooded seals are

Male hooded seal with inflated 'hood'.

Male hooded seal with inflated nasal septum.
Photo: R. Frank

Hooded seal 'family'. The male is considerably larger than the female. The pup is in the foreground.

involved in aggressive encounters or when humans approach males that are close to females on the ice. Females do not possess the 'hood', nor do they inflate red balloons.

Both male and female hooded seals have a bluish-grey coat marked with irregular black blotches that are less numerous on their silvery-grey bellies.

Unlike harp seals, male hooded seals are larger than females; both are considerably larger than harps. Adult males are about two and a half meters (over eight feet) long and weigh about 300 kilograms (660 pounds) whereas adult females are just over two meters (more than seven feet) long and weigh about 160 kilograms (350 pounds).

———————————*———————————

Several summers ago, one of our colleagues was passing through Fort Chimo (now known as Kuujjuaq), in the Ungava region of northern Quebec. A fellow traveller, a reporter for a national publication in Canada, asked him what he was doing in this isolated part of the world. Rob told him he was going north to study harp seals.

"Harp seals?," the reporter exclaimed, "I thought they were only in March!"

The reporter's somewhat bizarre comment nicely captures the fact that harp and hooded seals only enter the public consciousness for a few weeks each year. Once the seal hunt and the controversy that surrounds it subside, they fade from view and are forgotten for another year. This is unfortunate, for there is, as we shall see in the following chapters, much more to their biology and to their place in the history of the New World than their treatment as mere objects of killing and controversy would suggest.

2. Distribution and Migration

Mention harp seals (or hooded seals) and most people immediately associate them with the east coast of Canada, in particular with the coast of Newfoundland and the Gulf of St. Lawrence. Actually, both species are far more widely distributed than this, occurring throughout much of the north Atlantic Ocean.

Unlike some seal species that remain resident in one area throughout the entire year, both harp and hooded seals routinely undertake extensive annual migrations. Possibly because harp seals remain closer to shore, are much more numerous and move in groups, their annual cycle in the northwest Atlantic is quite well known. Less is known about other harp seal populations, and almost nothing is known about the precise movements of hooded seals throughout the year, except what can be inferred from their annual appearances on ice to give birth to their pups and to moult, and their occurrence in the catch statistics from various seal hunts. For these reasons, we will discuss the two species separately.

Harp seals

Harp seals are found in intimate association with ice and consequently the northern and southern limits of their annual range closely correspond to the seasonal limits of **pack ice** throughout the north Atlantic.

It is common practice to divide the world's harp seals into three separate populations, each identified with a different **breeding** site. Harp seals living in the northwest Atlantic off eastern Canada constitute the largest popula-

◀ Whitecoat.
Photo: N. Lightfoot

Harp seal distribution. Breeding sites are indicated by the four striped ovals.

tion. This population divides into two herds that breed on ice off the coast of Newfoundland and Labrador in an area known as the '**Front**' and near the Magdalen Islands (Isles de la Madeleine), which lie in the middle of the Gulf of St. Lawrence between Prince Edward Island and Newfoundland. These herds are commonly known as the 'Front herd' and '**Gulf** herd' respectively.

A second breeding population congregates on pack ice in the White Sea off the coast of the USSR. The third and smallest population comes together to 'pup' on the 'West Ice' between Jan Mayen and Svalbard (Spitsbergen).

Harp seal whelping patch.

Harp seals are also sighted along the coasts of Iceland, Norway and, occasionally, Great Britian.

Harp seals from all three populations exhibit similar patterns of annual migration, although the timing of events such as pupping (or **whelping**) varies from place to place. In the late autumn, they move southward ahead of the forming winter ice. After a period of winter feeding, adult females assemble by the thousands in their traditional whelping areas to give birth to their pups. Within days they transform several hundred square miles of transient pack ice into a huge, white nursery.

The northwest Atlantic harp seals give birth off the east coast of Canada from late February until mid-March with females on the Front pupping about five days later than females in the Gulf. The White Sea population whelps from mid-February until early March, whereas harp seals at Jan Mayen pup somewhat later, from mid-March until April.

Differences in the timing of whelping have been interpreted as evidence that the three populations are separate and that there is little interbreeding between them. Studies of skull and body dimensions add further support for the view that they are isolated breeding populations.

After weaning their pups, female harp seals join adult males to participate in the annual mating ritual, in preparation for the next whelping season. Adults from all three populations then begin to reassemble on ice north of the whelping patches to undergo the annual moult. At first, these '**moulting patches**' are composed almost entirely of adult males. During the days and weeks that follow, the adult males are joined by immature and other non-breeding animals from the north and eventually by adult females from the south. These moulting concentrations become extremely large and the animals are much closer together on the ice than during the whelping season. During the moult, each seal completely replaces its hair coat and the surface layers of skin.

Harp seal moulting patch.

After moulting, all three populations migrate northward to summer feeding grounds. The northwest Atlantic harp seals move along the Labrador coast toward Greenland (see Map) in late May and early June, feeding as they go. They are abundant during the summer months around Disco Island, the Thule area, Jones Sound, Lancaster Sound, and along the east coast of Baffin Island to the Hudson Strait, penetrating Hudson Bay at least as far south as Southampton Island. For animals that reach the northern end of the summer range, the annual migration represents a journey of over 5,000 kilometers (over 3,000 miles roundtrip).

Harp seal migration in the northwest Atlantic.

The pups complete their moult on the ice in the whelping patch and then slowly straggle northward independent of the older, experienced seals. What guides them during this maiden migration remains a mystery. Those born in the Gulf of St. Lawrence and off Newfoundland and Labrador tend to spend their first summer along the west coast of Greenland although some may be found in the eastern Canadian Arctic.

During the summer months, harp seals from Jan Mayen and the White Sea appear to mix to some degree; animals from both areas summer throughout the northern Barents and Kara Seas north of Svalbard, Franz Josef Land and Severnaya Zemlya.

In late September, adult seals begin to move southward once again. Intensive feeding takes place in the southern portions of their range from December to February and the seals accumulate fat reserves to meet the energy demands of the nursing, breeding and moulting periods that are to follow.

The annual migration involves almost all of the adults and some of the immatures. Many young animals and a few non-breeding adults appear to remain in northern waters throughout the year. In apparently rare instances, pregnant females may also forsake the southward migration. Such animals have been observed with their pups amidst large numbers of breeding hooded seals in the Davis Strait. On one occasion, two aberrant, out of season, summer births were reported in Arctic waters.

Hooded seals

Hooded seals share much of their range with harp seals. Except for a portion of the breeding season, however, the two species usually do not occur together. Hooded seals tend to remain farther offshore and feed in deeper water than harp seals. They rarely frequent land or shore-fast ice except in the Gulf of St. Lawrence.

Separate populations of hooded seals are less easily distinguished than are those of harp seals. Usually three populations are recognized and, as is the case with the harp seal, each is associated with a distinct breeding site.

One group whelps off the east coast of Canada, both on the Front and in the Gulf of St. Lawrence. On the Front, hooded seals usually congregate farther offshore than harp seals on heavier, drifting pack ice. In the Gulf of St. Lawrence a small number gather near dense concentrations of harp seals. Here, both species may even be seen together on the same pan of ice.

A second group of hooded seals also gathers with harp seals to reproduce on the West Ice off the island of Jan Mayen east of Greenland.

A third breeding site occurs in the Davis Strait between Greenland and Canada. Although hooded seals breeding here in the 1800s were hunted by Scottish whalers, it was only during the 1970s that this breeding concentration was 'rediscovered'.

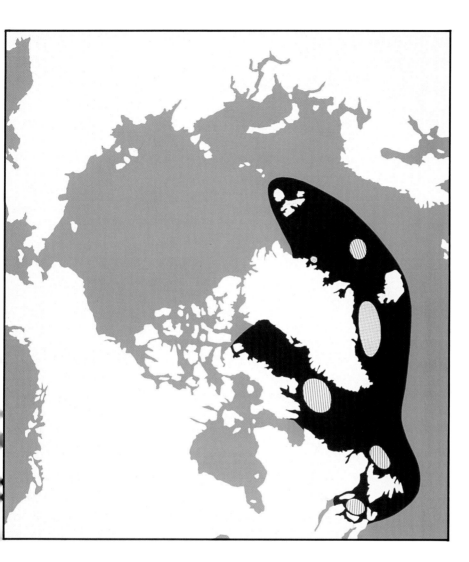

Hooded seal distribution. Breeding sites are indicated by the four striped ovals. Moulting occurs near the large stippled oval east of Greenland.

Hooded seals seem to wander more widely than harp seals and sometimes individuals, particularly juveniles, are found far beyond their normal range. Strays have been reported from the British Isles and along the European coast as far south as Portugal. Hooded seals are also seen in the St. Lawrence River west to Montreal, and have been reported along the eastern seaboard of the United States as far south as Cape Canaveral, Florida. In one celebrated instance in March 1974, a pregnant female hooded seal came ashore near South Brooksville, Maine; she gave birth to a pup and nursed it for four days before both animals mysteriously disappeared.

Infrequent sightings of scattered hooded seals have been reported throughout the islands of the eastern Canadian Arctic and a few animals have actually made it through the Northwest Passage to the Beaufort Sea. Hooded seals also wander into the Barents Sea and, rarely, along the coast of northern Siberia.

Like harp seals, hooded seals follow a seasonal migratory pattern. In February, adults congregate near thick ice in preparation for whelping and mating. Unlike those of harp seals, hooded seal births occur at the same time at all whelping locations, during the second half of March.

Blueback.
Photo: N. Lightfoot

The observation that hooded seals give birth at precisely the same time, regardless of location, has been interpreted as evidence that they all belong to a single breeding population, with individuals moving between breeding sites from year to year. Actually, there is little information on whether individual hooded seals move from one breeding site to another from one year to the next, or alternatively, whether they always return faithfully to the place of their birth. Such difficulties in defining distinct hooded seal populations present serious obstacles to scientists attempting to estimate how many hooded seals there are and to assess trends in their abundance.

After breeding, adult hooded seals move toward the Denmark Strait to moult in June, July and possibly August.

Following the moult, they disperse widely. Some move south and west around the southern tip of Greenland – Cape Farewell – then north along the coast of west Greenland as far as Thule. Others move to the east and north and are found in pack ice between Greenland and Svalbard during late summer and early fall.

Young hooded seals do not seem to follow the regular schedule of migration exhibited by their elders, although a few immatures may be seen at the fringes of whelping and breeding patches. The young of the year appear to avoid entirely the large moulting groups of adults.

Little else is known about the activities of hooded seals during the rest of the year. Each year a few are hunted during the winter in fjords near Angmagssalik, west Greenland. There are also reports that hooded seals have been seen feeding during the winter months on the Grand Banks off Newfoundland. But it is not until February that the hoods again reappear in large numbers in preparation for the next pupping season.

3. Life Cycles

During their lifetimes, organisms pass through a series of stages, each distinguished by a particular set of identifiable characteristics. In mammals such as seals, young animals are initially dependent on their mothers for food (milk) and protection. After a time, the youngsters, although still immature and growing, become more or less independent beings. They continue to grow and eventually reach the age of sexual maturity. Ultimately, they become adult members of the breeding population and, in producing their own offspring, complete a cycle – the life cycle – that ensures the continuity of generations over time.

In this chapter, we will describe the life cycles of harp and hooded seals. Some vital statistics for the two species are given in the table below. We will see that in some respects these two species have evolved quite different life cycles to overcome the problems associated with breeding in the pack-ice environment.

Harp seals

The **gregarious** nature of harp seals becomes immediately evident during the whelping season. When the '**whelping patch**' is first sighted, it is composed of scattered groups of females, some with their **newborn** pups, gathered around holes or leads in the ice that provide ready access to water. The 'patch' appears to grow in size as these early arrivals are joined by other pregnant females, apparently attracted to areas already occupied by mothers with young pups.

Each female harp seal will give birth to a single pup within days of her arrival on the southern pack ice. Twin foetuses have been reported but they are extremely rare

◀ Young female harp seal.
Photo: N. Lightfoot

Vital statistics of harp and hooded seals

	Harp seals	Hooded seals
Weight of adult females (kilograms)	130	160
Weight of adult males (kilograms)	130	300
Length of adult females (meters)	1.7	2.2
Length of adult males (meters)	1.7	2.5
Age at sexual maturity – females (years)	approx. 4	approx. 3
Age at sexual maturity – males (years)	approx. 4	approx. 5
Breeding system	promiscuity (?)	serial monogamy (?)
Life span (years)	approx. 30	approx. 30
Litter size	1	1
Pup weight at birth (kilograms)	10	20
Blubber at birth	no	yes
Colour at birth	white/yellow	'blue'/silver
Duration of lactation (days)	12	4
Growth rate of pup (kilograms/day)	2	5
Weight at weaning (kilograms)	34	40

1 kilogram = 2.2 pounds; 1 meter = 3.3 feet.

Whitecoat.

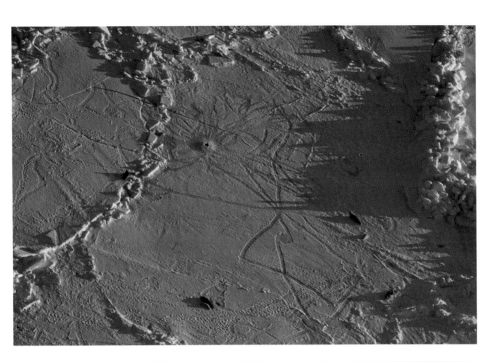

Harp seal whelping patch. Note the trails left by female harp seals as they return from the water through the hole in the ice (to the left of centre in the photograph).
Photo: S. Innes

Returning to the water.
Photo: N. Lightfoot

and it is highly unlikely that a female could produce enough milk to raise twins successfully.

The birth process is extremely rapid, frequently taking less than one minute. It is not usually preceded by any obvious labour. Pups are normally born hind flippers first, but head-first (cephalic) deliveries have also been observed. During delivery, the female quickly turns, leaving a characteristic spiral of birth-blood on the ice; the

Birth of a harp seal.

TOP LEFT: Pup appears, still enveloped in its amniotic sac.

TOP RIGHT: Pup emerges.

BOTTOM LEFT: Female immediately turns to nose her pup.

BOTTOM RIGHT: Newborn harp seal.

From a 16 mm movie filmed by N. Lightfoot, University of Guelph

'Birth spiral' on the whelping ice.

umbilical cord is often broken in the process. The spinning motion brings the female into immediate nose to nose contact with her offspring.

It is probably during this first face to face contact that the female harp seal learns the unique odour of her pup, information she will need to confirm its identity each time she returns to feed it. Over the next few days she will also learn its individual voice and perhaps to some extent its appearance.

A female harp seal feeds only her own pup. Adoption has never been documented. It is extremely important, therefore, that initial contacts between a mother and pup not be disturbed. If a female is forced to leave the ice before a bond has been formed with her pup, she may not recognize it upon returning to the ice. An abandoned pup faces certain death through starvation.

The harp seal pup, commonly known as a '**white-coat**', is undoubtedly the most photographed and best known of all seals. At birth it is about 92 centimeters (three feet) long and weighs, on average, nine to ten kilograms (20-22 pounds).

A well fed pup and a deserted starveling, both about ten days old.

During the birth process the pup experiences a sudden thermal shock. It is thrust from the thermostatically-controlled environment of the womb, maintained at a cosy 37°C (98.6°F), into a frigid white nursery where the environmental temperature may be well below freezing, and seems even colder because of the wind chill. Such conditions might be expected to cause considerable mortality among newborn harp seals but in fact only one or two per cent of pups are still-born or die of natural causes within the first few days of life. How the newborn pups manage to cope successfully with their new environment has been the subject of considerable scientific research.

Harp seal pups are born without the insulating blubber possessed by older animals and their wet hair provides little insulation. They initially warm themselves by shivering, but quite quickly switch to non-shivering thermogenesis, a process of heat production that, as its name suggests, does not involve shivering; rather, it involves the 'burning' of **'brown fat'** to release heat and warm the animal. Brown fat is found in many young mammals, including human babies; it is also used by many hibernators to warm up quickly after a long winter's sleep. Young harp seals do not depend on brown fat for very long, however, as pups begin to search for a meal of milk from mother almost immediately after birth, often while they are still wet with birth fluids. Suckling usually commences within a few hours after birth.

About half an hour after the pup is born, the female passes the placenta, a mass of blood vessels and connective tissue that is commonly called the 'afterbirth'. Circular in shape and about 30 centimeters (one foot) in diameter, the placentas may be seen scattered about the whelping patch.

A placenta.
Photo: N. Lightfoot

Unlike many other carnivores, including cats and dogs, seals do not eat their placentas. They are left on the ice and are consumed by gulls or become part of the marine **food web** when the ice melts.

During the first few weeks of life, young harp seals pass through a series of easily recognizable developmental

Age estimates associated with descriptive age categories of harp seal pups (see text for details)

Stage	Age (days)
Newborn	0
Yellowcoat	1
Thin whitecoat	4
Fat whitecoat	7
Greycoat	12
Ragged-jacket	21
Beater	25+

stages that provide an approximate guide to their age.

A newborn harp seal is not at all like the animal that is seen so frequently in newspapers, magazines and on the television news. It is small, skinny, uncoordinated and soaking wet, with all the appeal of a large, drowned rat. This stage is short-lived and within a day, the pup becomes more coordinated in its movements, its coat dries to a yellowish-white colour and fluffs up, and the little creature is transformed into something recognizable as a 'baby' seal. At this stage, it is appropriately termed a **'yellowcoat'**.

Newborn harp seal.

The coat of the newborn harp seal is actually foetal hair, or **lanugo**, which in most mammals, including humans, is shed in the womb prior to birth. In harp seals,

Yellowcoat.
Photo: N. Lightfoot

and the young of several other species of northern ice-breeding seals, this lanugo is highly developed and retained for almost two weeks as a luxuriant neonatal pelt. It gets its yellow coloration from the amniotic fluid which surrounds the pup in the uterus.

The yellow coloration only lasts for two or three days by which time it becomes washed off by rain or bleached by the sun. With the change in colour, the 'yellowcoat' becomes a **'thin whitecoat'**. By this time the pups are gaining weight at a rapid rate and appear stronger, less fragile and more coordinated in their movements.

Thin whitecoat.

Female harp seal checking on her pup.

Females remain with their pups almost continuously during the first few days after birth. After this time, however, their attendance drops substantially, to about 15 per cent of the time. Nonetheless, females do not stray far, usually maintaining visual contact with their offspring and only rarely moving out of hearing range. Females are often seen popping up in leads or holes in the ice to check on the whereabouts of their pups.

A number of factors influence the amount of time females spend on the ice. In addition to the pup's age, environmental factors such as temperature, wind velocity, cloud cover and ice conditions all affect the amount of time females spend out of the water.

Each female defends a small area around her pup, threatening other cows or pups that approach too closely. These exchanges rarely involve physical contact. Some females will also actively defend their pups against humans, such as sealers, scientists or tourists who approach them or their pups too closely, although the majority will take to the water under these circumstances.

Aggressive encounter between two female harp seals.

Female harp seal defending her pup.
Photo: N. Lightfoot

Normally, when confronted by a threatening female harp seal it is best to simply stop, and move quietly in another direction making sure that you do not block her access to the water. On rare occasions when a female harp seal charges a person who gets too close, the only real option is to flee as quickly as possible. On glare ice, wriggling females are not nearly as awkward as they are usually portrayed; well developed nails on their fore flippers provide excellent traction as the seals slither over the slippery ice at remarkable speed. And their enlarged canine teeth can inflict a nasty bite.

Female harp seal threatening cameraman.
Photo: N. Lightfoot

Like most babies, harp seal pups spend most of their time on the ice asleep. Individual pups commonly use only one or two resting spots and, if undisturbed, remain very close to where their mothers left them. They are so sedentary that on sunny days they melt the ice beneath them, creating body-shaped cradles in the ice.

Ice cradle.
Photo: N. Lightfoot

Nap time.

Often pups wake only when it is time to feed. They are fed every few hours throughout the day and probably throughout the night as well. When they are hungry they bawl, in a remarkably human 'mmoooooomm' fashion. This cry is usually answered quickly by the appearance of the female. Nursing sessions last about ten minutes, until either the female moves away or the satiated pup stops suckling.

Fat harp seal pup in ice cradle.

Pup calling mom.

A newborn pup has obvious difficulties locating the nipples and spends time searching and prodding its mother's entire abdominal area. Once it locates the nipples, the young pup still has some difficulty remaining upright long enough to nurse. It soon becomes much more adept at nursing and, within a day or two after birth, learns to locate the nipples quickly and becomes proficient at moving between the two teats.

Nursing is almost always preceded by the female nosing the pup to confirm its identity. Some females entice their pups to relocate just prior to a nursing bout by letting them find the nipples and then moving several meters away. This is repeated, sometimes again and again, and the hungry pup quickly follows, usually protesting loudly. Once permitted to nurse, the pups position themselves at right angles to the female and brace themselves on the ice with their fore flippers.

Female harp seal identifying her pup, *Photo: R.E.A. Stewart*

Female harp seal leading pup.

Female harp seal
nursing a yellowcoat.

Female harp seal
nursing a fat whitecoat.

Harp seal pups grow quickly on the fat rich milk
their mothers liberally provide for them. By the time of
weaning, the fat content of harp seal milk reaches at least
40 per cent, eight to ten times the fat content of cows' milk.
In appearance, harp seal milk resembles cream-coloured
yogurt; it has an oily texture and a very strong fishy taste.

On their high calorie diets, thin whitecoats are transformed into '**fat whitecoats**' by the time they are a week
old. Rapid weight gain continues throughout the nursing
period. Pups increase in weight by approximately two kilograms (more than four pounds) per day. More than half of
this weight is stored directly as fat. By the end of the nursing period, which normally lasts less than two weeks, pups

Fat whitecoat.

weigh more than 30 kilograms (66 pounds) – some individuals actually top more than 45 kilograms (100 pounds) – and have a blubber layer that may be five centimeters (two inches) thick.

At about the time of weaning – when the females stop nursing – pups become known as '**greycoats**' because their spotted, grey juvenile **pelage** has grown in and can be seen underneath the white coat. It is at about this time that females come into mating condition.

Weaning is abrupt and not preceded by any change in the pattern of nursing. Females simply leave, as they normally would between nursing bouts, but this time, they never return. The pups continue to call frequently for a

Greycoat.

day or two, but adjust to their mothers' absence quickly and soon become extremely quiet and **sedentary**.

During the time when pups are being born and nursed, adult males keep their distance, gathering in small, dense groups clustered around holes and leads. Early in the whelping season any concentration of adult seals without any white-coated pups is almost certainly a group of

Male harp seals.
TOP: From the air.
Photo: R. Frank
BOTTOM LEFT: In a lead.
BOTTOM RIGHT: On the ice.

males. Male harp seals can be positively distinguished from females because they appear to have two belly-buttons, one of which is actually the penile opening.

Toward the end of **lactation**, the males begin to circulate through the whelping patch in search of females

Identifying the sexes. The male (TOP) has a belly-button and a penile opening. The female (BOTTOM) has a belly-button and two teats leaking milk.

that are ready to mate. Males and females appear to mate promiscuously, without any prolonged pair-bonding. Although vigorous courtship behaviour, such as males chasing females and biting at their hindquarters, may be observed on the ice, copulation usually takes place in the water.

Courtship and attempted copulation on the ice.

Battle-scared male harp seal in the whelping patch.

The fertilized egg resulting from successful mating will eventually develop into next year's pup. In harp seals the newly fertilized egg divides several times forming a multicelled, spherical embryo which then floats free in the womb for about three and a half months before it implants in the wall of the uterus. This type of 'suspended' development is known as delayed implantation.

In species with a short, well defined breeding season, delayed implantation assures that all females give birth to their offspring at the same time each year. This is particularly important for harp and hooded seals that depend on short-lived pack ice as a whelping substrate.

Once the embryo becomes implanted in the womb, it grows rapidly for the next eight months. During this time the pregnant female spends the summer feeding in the north before returning south in the fall and giving birth precisely 12 months after her last pup was born.

Within days of mating, adult harp seals begin to disappear from the whelping patch, leaving the weaned pups to fend for themselves.

The entire process of birth, nursing and mating for the following year is thus accomplished in about two weeks. This is incredibly fast for such a large mammal. Dogs and cats require about six weeks and even rats and mice take 21 days to wean their young.

The rapid development of harp seal pups allows for a short period of maternal care. This provides several advantages for female harp seals. They are able to rear their young in a temporary pack-ice environment, safe from many terrestrial predators – excepting the polar bear in some areas – while minimizing the time that they are tied

Annual cycle of an adult female harp seal, showing the timing of important reproductive events.

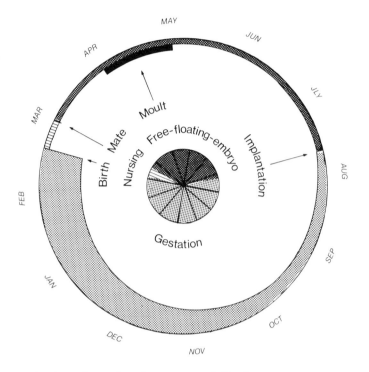

to the ice where they have some difficulty moving.

The nursing period is extremely costly to a female harp seal. Because she is not feeding during this time, she must not only support herself, but also her pup, entirely on the energy she has stored in blubber beneath the skin prior to the breeding season. As a result, a female will lose more than three kilograms (more than six and a half pounds) per day during lactation. By the time she leaves her pup she will have lost more than one quarter of her total body weight.

Lean female harp seal.

Around the time that pups are weaned by their mothers, their white hair becomes loose and several days later it begins to fall out. During this moult, pups have a ragged appearance with the smooth, short juvenile pelage exposed between patches of long fluffy white fur. This **'ragged-jacket'** phase lasts a week or more.

Ragged-jacket.

The loss of the white coat raises questions about its significance. Many animals living in cold climates have white winter coats. Such coats are thought to provide camouflage that enhances the ability to hunt (e.g. polar bears) or reduces the risk of being hunted (e.g. collared lemmings), or both (e.g. weasels). Accordingly, it has been suggested that the white colour of the fur of young harp

Polar bear searching for harp seals.
Photo: R. Frank

seals, being the same colour as their nursery, provides protective coloration. This seems unlikely, however, for the pups do not attempt to conceal themselves; they frequently remain out in the open and, regardless of their colour, their loud cries would make them vulnerable to any hunting predator with reasonable hearing, even if it were blind.

For the harp seal pup, its transparent white hairs seem to be more important for keeping warm than for protection from predators. The structure and colour of the individual hairs enhance their ability to capture sunlight for additional warmth on sunny days. The white lanugo, in addition to acting as an insulating blanket around the pup, also transmits and reflects the sunlight down through the pelt where it is absorbed at or near the surface of the dark skin.

A well insulated whitecoat does not lose sufficient heat to melt the snow from last night's storm.

As testimony to the effectiveness of the white pelt in using sunlight (solar radiation) as an external heat source, skin temperatures as high as 41°C (106°F) have been recorded in young seals lying on the whelping ice, despite the fact that their deep body temperature is only about 37°C (98.6°F) and the air temperature may be close to freezing. The warm skin then radiates heat (thermal infrared radiation) that warms up the air within the pelt. This 'greenhouse' effect not only reduces the amount of heat pups lose to the environment, but as a consequence, conserves energy by reducing the amount of precious milk that must be used to keep the pup warm. It is only after weaning, when pups have developed a thick layer of insulating blubber, that the white coat is shed.

When the white coat is completely moulted and the black-spotted, silvery-grey pelt of the immature harp seal is fully exposed, the pup then becomes known as a **'beater'**. The term 'beater' supposedly refers to the poorly developed swimming skills of these young animals that 'beat' the surface of the water when they first attempt to swim and dive. Most beaters remain on the ice until it breaks up or is carried away by the currents. Weaned pups do not feed at this time. They fast, living on energy stores accumulated during the nursing period. These energy stores carry them through the moult and sustain them until they enter the water and learn to swim and forage on their own.

Beater.

When pups finally take to the water they eventually begin to feed, primarily on small shrimp-like crustaceans called euphausids. As their swimming skills increase, they broaden the spectrum of their diet to include a wide variety of larger crustaceans (zooplankton) and small fish.

Beaters are seen scattered along the ice edge off the east coasts of Newfoundland and Labrador during the adult moulting period. They seem to make their way by moving from one pan of ice to the next, following the receding ice northward.

Beaters moult the next spring, at the age of 13-14 months. The beater pelt is replaced with a similar spotted pelt but once again the juvenile harp seal changes its name, this time to **'bedlamer'**, from the French *bête de la mer*, meaning 'beast of the sea'.

Bedlamer – the spotted animal in the foreground.

Harp seals remain bedlamers until the spots on the immature pelt start to disappear and the harp-shaped pattern of the adult begins to emerge on the back. This final change in pelage pattern begins with the onset of sexual maturity (the time known as puberty among humans). Most male harp seals develop the harp marking abruptly, whereas in females it appears more gradually over several years. Some females may never lose all their spots or develop a complete black harp.

Pelage patterns in older harp seals.
LEFT: bedlamer.
CENTRE: spotted harp.
RIGHT: old harp.

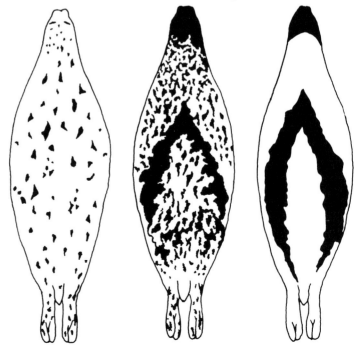

In many animals, particularly females, the spotted bedlamer pattern may coexist with the faint outline of the emerging harp. The spots fade as the harp darkens to form the adult pattern. Animals in the process of transition from the bedlamer pelt to the adult harp are known as '**spotted harps**'.

Old female harp seal.
Photo: N. Lightfoot

Spotted harp.

44

'Sooty' male harp seal.

Neonatal mortality.

TOP LEFT: Stillborn.
Photo: S. Innes

TOP RIGHT: Abandoned starveling.

BOTTOM LEFT: Birth defect.
Photo: N. Lightfoot

BOTTOM RIGHT: Accidental death from being trapped under the ice and snow.
Photo: S. Innes

▼Adult mortality.

LEFT: Crushed in the shifting ice.

RIGHT: Predation by polar bears on the Front.

A few individuals never develop the harp pattern, but remain spotted or darkly streaked. These animals are referred to as 'smutty' or 'sooty' seals.

Harp seals become sexually mature at about four years of age. Females can thus give birth to their first pups shortly after their fifth birthday. Males do not usually breed until they are six or seven years old. A normal life span for both sexes is 30 to 35 years.

For centuries, hunting by humans has been by far the greatest cause of mortality among harp seals of all ages and this will be discussed in some detail in Chapter 5. Natural causes of neonatal mortality include stillbirths, starvation and crushing or drowning under shifting ice. During the first year of life, natural mortality is thought to be between 20 and 30 per cent. After the first year, it begins to drop, to about 10 per cent per year in older seals. Polar bears, Greenland sharks and killer whales all take unknown numbers of harp seals of all ages. Parasites and disease are not thought to be common causes of death.

Hooded seals

Like harp seals, female hooded seals give birth to a single pup each year. Twins have never been reported. The larger size of hooded seals is evident at birth. The pups are about 105 centimeters (just over three feet) long and weigh about 20 kilograms (44 pounds). Young hooded seals have a somewhat flattened appearance with huge, dark eyes.

Hooded seal placenta surrounded by dark hair discs.
Photo: N. Lightfoot

Unlike harp seals, hooded seal pups shed their light grey lanugo prior to birth. The free-floating hair is apparently swallowed by the fetus, passed through the digestive system and formed into compact little discs of hair that are frequently seen on the ice near the newborns.

Hooded seal pups are thus born with their immature pelt (corresponding to the beater pelt in harp seals). It is this luxuriant pelt, blue-grey on the back and silver-grey on the sides and underneath, and once the most valuable pelt to the sealing industry, that gives the hooded seal pup its common name, **'blueback'**.

Newborn hooded seal. Note the yellow stain from the amniotic fluids as seen in newborn harp seals. Hair discs can be seen in the background.
Photo: N. Lightfoot

Blueback.
Photo: N. Lightfoot

The birth process of hooded seals is very different from that of harp seals. Hooded seal females select an isolated spot within a loose aggregation of other female hooded seals. They usually remain at least 50 meters (150 feet) away from other individuals and well away from open water, often in the middle of a large pan of ice. Birth takes place after a relatively long labour, during which females undergo prolonged bouts of strong contractions. Hooded seal cows do not turn during the delivery but lie motionless on their sides after the pup is born and appear quite fatigued.

Hooded seal female and pup shortly after birth.
Photo: N. Lightfoot

Blueback showing umbilical cord. The pup has also been tagged on the hind flipper as part of a research program conducted by the Canadian Government.
Photo: N. Lightfoot

The differences in labour and delivery between harp and hooded seals may be due in part to the larger size of the hooded seal pup relative to its mother. They may also reflect evolutionary differences between the two species. Female hooded seals are not as gregarious as harp seal females. The female hooded seal is usually sufficiently far away from other females when she gives birth that there is no possibility of confusing her pup with those of her neighbours. Furthermore, because hooded seal cows never leave their pups during the nursing period, there has been no need to develop the ability to recognize individual pups; in normal, undisturbed situations, the pup beside a cow will always be her own.

Two female hooded seals with their pups. *Photo: N. Lightfoot*

Compared to harp seal pups, bluebacks are born in an extremely advanced state of development. In addition to having completed their first moult prior to birth, they already have a thin blubber layer to keep them warm. They are also capable of coordinated movements such as swimming and crawling shortly after birth. Male pups are larger than females and this size difference persists throughout life.

Female hooded seal defending her pup.

Female hooded seals are extremely protective of their young. Numerous references in old sealing memoirs refer to their 'fearless devotion' to their offspring. In hooded seals, such defense of young may be necessary for the pup's survival. Mother-pup pairs are attended by one or more aggressive males that compete fiercely for proximity to the female and eventually for mating privileges, with no regard for her youngster. The males perform spectacular displays involving the hood and the crimson red balloon in an attempt to deter and dissuade potential competitors as well as to impress the female who is the object of their attention. When the balloon is inflated, the male shakes it violently, making a loud 'pinging' noise in the process.

Displaying male hooded seals.

Photo: N. Lightfoot

Photo: N. Lightfoot

If acoustic and visual displays do not discourage their opponents, male hooded seals will resort to open combat, biting, pushing and clawing each other. Consequently male hooded seals commonly bear open wounds during the breeding season.

Combat. Male hooded seals fighting on the ice and in the water. *LEFT photo: R. Frank*

Battle scars. *RIGHT photo: R. Frank*

Despite the larger size of males and their ferocity toward each other, it is interesting that females, although smaller, seem to have little difficulty intimidating them. Females keep the males away from their pups, vigorously attacking those that approach too closely.

Female hooded seal threatening a suitor.

The encounters between male hooded seals usually end with a single victor remaining on the ice near the female and her pup. These scattered trios are commonly referred to as 'families'. This is a misnomer because the male is almost certainly not the father of this year's pup, although he undoubtedly aspires to be the father of next year's pup.

Female hooded seal nursing her pup with an adult male waiting in the background.

If the short nursing period and rapid pup growth and development of harp seals are impressive, their accomplishments pall in comparison to those of hooded seals. It has recently been discovered that hooded seals have the shortest lactation period known for any mammal. Pups are fed for an average of only four days.

Satiated. A young hooded seal just after dinner.
Photo: N. Lightfoot

This discovery explains the mysterious disappearance of the hooded seal female and her pup from the coast of Maine in 1975 after only four days (see Chapter 2, p. 17). Although this particular female chose a peculiar place to give birth to her pup, she nursed it for the normal time before departing. Usually, the pup would stay put for a while after weaning, but in this instance, it presumably departed its place of birth shortly after its mother had left, possibly to escape the attention of curious onlookers on the beach.

Despite the short nursing period, hooded seal pups still more than double their birth weight, growing at the incredible rate of more than five kilograms (11 pounds) per day. Once again this extremely fast rate of growth is achieved because of the large amounts of very fat-rich milk that the female provides for her offspring, using only her stored body fat. Hooded seal milk is more than 50 per cent fat.

A recently weaned blueback.

After the pups are weaned, adult hooded seals mate. The new embryo goes through a dormant phase similar to that described for the harp seal. After mating, the adults disperse from the whelping areas and their activities remain largely unknown until they recongregate during the summer to moult (see Chapter 2, p. 18).

Hooded seal pups remain behind on the whelping ice, eventually entering the water and making their way slowly northward. They are frequently seen along the edge of the pack ice in April, near concentrations of moulting harp seals.

Hooded seal pups lose their 'blueback' pelt during their first **post-natal** moult when they are approximately 14 months old. Little else is known about the habits of juvenile hooded seals until they reach maturity.

Female hooded seals reach sexual maturity somewhat earlier than harp seals, at about the age of three years. Many can therefore give birth for the first time on or about their fourth birthday. From this time on, most will produce a single pup each year for the remainder of their lives. Male hooded seals reach sexual maturity at four to six years of age, but probably cannot compete successfully with older males for mates until they are considerably older.

A young male hooded seal.

Maximum life spans of hooded seals are in the order of 35 years and, as with humans, the larger males are thought to have shorter life spans than the smaller females.

Presumed rates of natural mortality for adults range from seven to 15 per cent per year depending on the method of estimation. Predators of the hooded seal are likely the same as those of the harp seal – polar bears on whelping patches, Greenland sharks and perhaps killer whales. In recent centuries, humans have been their major known predator.

4. Adaptations for Life in the Sea

During the last 30 million years, seals have evolved from their terrestrial ancestors into truly aquatic beasts. This has required changes in almost every aspect of their lives. In order to survive, they have had to make anatomical, physiological and behavioural adjustments to meet the demands imposed by the marine environment.

To begin to understand just how extensive the changes have been, remember the last time that you, a terrestrial mammal, went to the beach. You probably read a book; a dog barked and you looked in its direction. The odour of suntan oil or seaweed reached your nostrils. After some time in the sun, you got uncomfortably warm; you walked toward the sea. As soon as your feet touched the water, you paused. Although its temperature may have been warm, it felt cold. You moved into deeper water and the deeper it got, the more difficult it became to walk; you took the plunge and dove in.

Immediately, a refreshing chill swept through your body; you forgot that you had been too warm. You returned quickly to the surface to breathe. You dove again and opened your eyes under water. Even if you were swimming in the clearest of water, you had a great deal of difficulty seeing anything well with your 'terrestrial eyes'. Certainly you could not read under these conditions even if you had a waterproof book. Sounds no longer came from one direction but seemed to surround you. You smelled nothing. You surfaced again to breathe.

Perhaps you were not content to paddle or swim near the water's edge and ventured into deeper and possibly colder water for longer periods of time. Think about the

Treading water.
Photo: W. Curtsinger –
IFAW

Bill Curtsinger, on
assignment with the
National Geographic
Society, prepares to go
diving with harp seals
in the Gulf of St.
Lawrence.
*Photo: K. McVeigh,
Graphics Division,
Environment Canada*

preparations you had to make – a wet suit or a dry suit to
combat the cold, a mask to protect your eyes and to
improve your vision under water, a weight belt to counteract buoyancy, swim fins to make movement easier, and a
snorkel or tanks of compressed air to enable you to keep
your head submerged for more than a minute or two. And
despite all of these technological adaptations, you still had
to take precautions to avoid a variety of lurking dangers
such as the **'bends'** (decompression sickness or **caisson
disease**) and the **'rapture of the deep'** (nitrogen narcosis).
If any of the above experiences is familiar to you, you have
some fleeting appreciation of what confronted the early
ancestors of modern pinnipeds when they first dipped
their toes tentatively into the water.

Several hypotheses have been proposed to explain
why the ancestors of pinnipeds turned their attention
toward the seas. Perhaps they were seeking refuge from
land predators. More likely, newly abundant food
resources along some shorelines were simply too enticing
to resist. Pinnipeds first appear in the fossil record at a
time of marked increases in coastal upwellings some 23
million years ago. Such upwellings bring nutrients from
the ocean's depths to the surface, resulting in a surge of
plant life (primary productivity) that can support a rich
diversity of animal forms, including zooplankton and fish,
upon which seals depend for their food.

Whatever combination of conditions encouraged the
ancestors of seals to spend time in the water, these ances-

tors ultimately became dependent on the seas for their food. Yet, unlike the **whales**, the pinnipeds have never entirely broken the bonds with *terra firma*. While this may seem like having the best of both worlds, it nonetheless requires that pinnipeds must be capable of functioning in two very different environments – air and water. Thus, while evolving to live in water, they had to retain certain features that allowed them to cope in air, creating the unique combination of aquatic and terrestrial features that characterize the pinnipeds.

Walruses on Round Island, Alaska.
Photo: E.H. Miller

In the following sections we will examine how the pinnipeds have adapted for their amphibious life-style. Because understanding adaptations is best accomplished through comparison, we will concentrate on the principal differences between seals and their terrestrial relatives, differences that have resulted from their millions of years of separate evolution. Since the fossil record is limited, we will not attempt to discuss precisely how things changed, but rather, we will describe the present day outcome – seals.

Thermoregulation

The refreshing chill that you experienced as the swimmer in our beach scenario identifies a potentially deadly problem for any warm-blooded mammal that intends to spend extended periods of time in the sea. Water can rapidly drain heat from warm bodies not equipped to prevent it. This cooling effect is due to the fact that the 'thermal conductivity' of water is more than 20 times greater than that of air. In order to maintain the constant and relatively warm deep-body temperature of 37°C (98.6°F), which is characteristic of mammals including humans, warm-blooded animals must balance their heat losses to the environment with internal heat production (metabolism). Lacking the technological adaptations available to human divers today, early marine mammals had to evolve biological adaptations to prevent excessive heat loss in order to survive in their new environment.

All truly warm-blooded creatures evolved on land. Generally, such animals reduce heat loss by surrounding themselves with a layer of insulation. Birds accomplish this with a covering of feathers; mammals, normally with a covering of hair. Such insulators take advantage of the low thermal conductivity of air to reduce heat loss when environmental air temperatures drop. In water, however, feathers and hair lose their insulative properties, unless they are waterproofed by oily secretions from glands in the skin.

Among the pinnipeds, the pelts of the fur seals and sea lions are most similar to those of terrestrial mammals. Fur seals, as their name implies, retain a well developed

North Pacific fur seal. Note the thick pelt.
Photo: E.H. Miller

coat. This coat is made up of long, coarse hairs overlying an extremely thick and dense woolly underfur that traps a layer of air to insulate the animal. In water, the fur seal's oily coat, like that of the beaver and muskrat, retains the ability to keep this layer of air between the hairs for insulation.

The sea lions are larger animals that tend to live in warmer climates. Generally, they have thinner coats than those of fur seals. In both fur seals and sea lions, the insulation provided by the pelt is supplemented by a layer of blubber just beneath the skin.

California sea lion. Note the smooth pelt. *Photo: D. Costa*

As with many other traits, the **true seals** exhibit more extreme modifications of their body insulation for life in water than do the fur seals and sea lions. While they too retain a hair coat, it is made up of short stiff hairs overlying a thin but dense layer of woolly underfur. Seals such as the monk seals and northern elephant seal, which live in warmer climates, have lost the woolly underfur and consequently have thinner coats than true seals living in colder climates. However, unlike the pelts of fur seals and sea lions, those of the true seals are not waterproofed; they become fully wetted and hence provide virtually no insulation in water.

Northern elephant seal during moult. Note the pealing patches of short, dense hair. *Photo: E.H. Miller*

The loss of insulation associated with the reduction of the pelt in true seals is compensated for by the addition of an even thicker layer of blubber than that found in fur seals and sea lions. The blubber not only supplements the insulation provided by the pelt in air, but is the main source of insulation in water. As a bonus, blubber also provides a rich source of stored energy that can be used when food is in short supply. In addition, it rounds out body contours to streamline the seal, easing its movements through the water.

Naked walruses.
Photo: E.H. Miller

The walrus has forsaken its fur coat almost completely, depending entirely on a thick layer of blubber under the skin for insulation, both in air and in water. This is a condition shared with whales.

The blubber layer in seals (and whales) is not merely a passive insulator like the fiberglass insulation in your house. Rather it is supplied with blood vessels that permit the animals to regulate heat loss to the environment. When in cold water the blood vessels of the blubber layer and skin contract to reduce blood flow to the surface. Just enough blood is allowed to reach the skin to prevent it from freezing. This minimizes heat loss but requires that the skin of seals be able to tolerate much colder temperatures than that of many other mammals.

For example, in humans, skin temperature is maintained at about 33.8°C (93°F) when the deep body temper-

An Innuk on Baffin Island skins an immature harp seal, revealing the thick layer of blubber underneath.

ature is a normal 37°C (98.6°F). When heat loss is increased, as happens when we go swimming, the temperature of the skin immediately drops. We begin to feel uncomfortably cold when our skin temperature falls to 31°C (88°F) and will probably begin to shiver if it reaches 27°C (81°F) (shivering is a response of the body to increase the rate of heat production). A skin temperature as low as 16°C (60°F) may cause extreme pain in some regions of the body. In contrast, skin temperatures of seals normally drop close to 0°C (32°F) without causing any undue suffering.

The flippers of pinnipeds, like the legs of many birds and mammals, also serve to regulate heat loss from the animal. This is accomplished by means of 'counter-current heat exchangers' in which veins returning blood from the flippers to the heart first pass near arteries delivering blood from the heart to the periphery. This arrangement of blood vessels permits the transfer of heat from the warmer arterial blood to the cooler venous blood so that body heat is retained, rather than being lost to the environment.

Additionally, at least some seals, such as the harp seal, have brown fat deposits around the blood vessels that carry cooled blood from the periphery of the body to the heart. When necessary, this brown fat can be used to generate heat to warm the blood in much the same way that newborn seals use brown fat for rapid heat production.

The arrangement of blood vessels close to the surface of the flippers also serves a special thermoregulatory function when the animals are on land. In cold temperatures, increased blood flow near the surface allows the seals to absorb significant amounts of heat when basking in the sun. Of course, the enriched supply of blood vessels in the flippers also permits rapid cooling if the seal begins to overheat.

Various behavioural strategies are also employed by pinnipeds to conserve heat. For example, many species will keep their fore flippers pressed against the body and their hind flippers closed and pressed together in order to reduce heat loss. Some species, such as the walrus, huddle together in dense congregations. Such behaviour may reduce heat loss, in addition to serving a number of social functions.

Atlantic walruses huddle together on Coats Island in the Northwest Territories.
Photo: E.H. Miller

Despite all of these adaptations for conserving heat in cold environments, and particularly in water, it has long been believed that marine mammals must also have higher rates of metabolic heat production, in comparison to those of other mammals, in order to stay warm in water. Consequently, the argument is that marine mammals must eat greater amounts of food than their terrestrial counterparts in order to fuel the high metabolic demands imposed by their aquatic life-styles. Although these views are well entrenched in the scientific literature, recent evidence indicates that marine mammals do not have higher **metabolic rates**, nor do they require more food, than do terrestrial mammals.

Adult pinnipeds are large animals. This alone helps to conserve heat because large bodies actually have relatively smaller surface areas exposed to the environment than do small bodies. The large body size of marine mammals, in combination with the well developed layer of insulation and the circulatory and behavioural adjustments mentioned above, means that the major problem for seals and whales may not, in fact, be heat conservation. Ironically, the problem may be how to dissipate sufficient amounts of heat to maintain a constant deep body temperature, especially for seals when they are on land.

When pinnipeds begin to overheat, they can increase the blood flow to the flippers, dilate blood vessels in the blubber or simply enter the water to increase the rate of heat loss to the environment and regulate their body temperature. Some species, such as the northern elephant seal, which inhabit beaches, lose heat by flippering cool sand onto themselves or by lying in the shade or on cool wet sand to prevent overheating. Others will expose as much of their bodies as possible to circulating air to lose heat through convection.

Northern elephant seals on a California beach.
Photo: D. Costa

A solitary ringed seal peaks up through a hole in the ice.
Photo: J. Hickie

Thus, while cold water represents an inhospitable, indeed a potentially lethal environment for humans and most other mammals, the marine mammals have evolved adaptations to counteract the cooling properties of water. To the envy of humans, and particularly of those who enjoy diving, well fed and well insulated pinnipeds are normally quite comfortable, whether they are lying on the sand beaches of California or swimming in frigid seas off eastern Canada.

Locomotion

Overcoming the problems of losing body heat in water permitted the pinnipeds to stay in the sea for prolonged periods. There remained, however, the problem of moving efficiently in the ocean. Speed and endurance are essential in order to elude potential predators and to catch prey. Although most mammals can swim to some degree, and the world marvelled at the swimming exploits of Mark Spitz at the 1972 summer Olympics, few – including Spitz with his seven gold medals – have the ability to make a living hunting for food in the sea.

The pinnipeds can, having evolved remarkable swimming abilities. They are as efficient in water as many fish species despite their need to retain some facility for movement on land or ice. Generally, they have accomplished this through modifications of the typical mammalian body plan, most obviously through changing their body form into a streamlined shape and turning their limbs into flippers.

The layer of blubber beneath the skin ensures that their body contours are smooth, reducing drag and making movement through water relatively easy. Even their small tails are neatly tucked between the hind flippers during swimming and the genitals are either internal or retractable so that their body contours are not interrupted during swimming.

To provide the power required for movement in water, the bones of the fore and hind limbs have become shortened and only the regions beyond the elbow or the ankle emerge from the body. The 'hands' and 'feet' have also been extensively modified to form the flippers. The fingers and toes of the hands and feet have become greatly elongated, surrounded by fatty, fibrous tissue, and joined by skin that forms a 'web' between the fingers and toes.

The flippers provide a large surface area to propel the animal through the water or to serve as rudders for steering. Along with these modifications, the claws of most seals tend to be reduced in size, although ice-breeding seals, such as harp and hooded seals, retain strong claws on the fore flippers to help the animals move over the slippery surface.

Characteristic differences in the limbs of the three pinniped families noted in Chapter 1 not only reflect evolutionary differences (and interrelationships) within the group, but also influence the modes of swimming exhibited by fur seals and sea lions, the walrus, and the true seals.

Among the fur seals and the sea lions, the fore flippers provide propulsion while the hind flippers serve mainly as rudders for steering in the water. Consequently, watching these pinnipeds in water gives one the impression more of flight than of swimming. Their necks remain

A California sea lion 'flies' by.
Photo: M. Neumann – Photo Researchers

strong and, compared to those of other pinnipeds, relatively long.

With limited modifications of the limbs for swimming, fur seals and sea lions are still able to walk on land with their bodies held above the ground. At slow speeds the fore and hind flippers move in alternate pairs (like a trotter) while at high speeds both fore flippers, then both hind flippers, bear the weight, creating a sinuous galloping gait.

Swimming harp seal. Note the hind flippers. *Photo: W. Curtsinger – IFAW*

More committed to an aquatic existence, the **phocid** seals exhibit more specialized adaptations for movement in water. In these true seals, the power that drives the body through the water comes primarily from the hind flippers. These are alternately expanded and contracted while being pushed from side to side by the strong muscles of the lower back and hind limbs. The fore flippers, which are small in comparison to those of the **otariids**, are held pressed against the body during fast swimming and are used mainly for steering when the animal wants to change direction. When the seal is swimming more slowly, the fore flippers are sometimes used like paddles and, when the seal is stationary, they can be moved in a sculling motion to stabilize the animal in the water. The neck of phocids is shorter than that of otariids, tending to merge with the remainder of the body. A long neck would be impractical for an animal 'driven' from the rear.

On land or ice, the phocids are much less agile than otariids. Harp and hooded seals, like most other northern phocids, use their fore flippers together or alternately to grip the ice, rock or sand, pulling their bodies along afterwards. When moving quickly on snow or sand, however, they virtually 'swim' over the surface, with their bodies moving quickly from side to side. As a result, they leave a snake-like trail behind them.

The intermediate position of the walrus family in the evolution of the pinnipeds is perhaps most obviously reflected in their limb structure and modes of locomotion. The structure of the hind flipper resembles that of the true seals but, as noted earlier, like the fur seals and sea lions, the walrus can bring its flippers forward underneath the body to walk on land. In water, the walrus may paddle with its fore flippers in the manner of fur seals and sea lions or propel itself by moving the hind flippers in a lateral motion as do the true seals.

Of course, swimming is but one aspect of making a living in the sea. In order to exploit the three-dimensional marine environment successfully, marine mammals must also be able to dive.

Diving

The diving abilities of seals have long been of great human interest, and hence, the subject of considerable study by scientists. Much of the interest stems from the fact that marine mammals seem unbothered by many of the problems encountered by human divers, including the need for a virtually constant supply of air to breathe and problems associated with pressure at depth.

At best, most humans can hold their breath for about one minute. With practice, some people can increase this to two or two and a half minutes, but rarely longer. Most other terrestrial mammals cannot do much better. Of course, the limiting factor is the need for oxygen.

All mammals require a constant supply of oxygen that is obtained from the air they breathe. Yet some marine mammals can hold their breath while diving under water for astounding periods of time. Among the pinnipeds, dive times last as long as five to eight minutes in fur seals and sea lions and ten minutes in the walrus. But it is in the phocid seals that truly impressive dive times have been recorded (for a summary of average and maximum dive times for a variety of pinnipeds, see the accompanying Table). Smaller phocids, such as the Arctic ringed seal, the temperate coastal harbour (or common) seal and the harp seal, all have maximum dive times in the region of 15 to 30 minutes. Maximum dive duration in the northern elephant seal is about 40 minutes. The record holder is the Weddell seal in the Antarctic, where the longest recorded dive by an individual animal lasted for one hour and 13 minutes.

In comparison, the world record for humans staying under water voluntarily (and living to tell the story), listed in *The Guinness Book of Records* (1987), was set by Robert Foster, a 32-year old electronics technician from Richmond, California. On 15 March 1959, dressed in a complete wet suit including a hood and face mask, he remained stationary, three meters (ten feet) under water, anchored to the bottom of the swimming pool at the Bermuda Palms Motel in San Rafael, California, for 13 minutes, 42.5 seconds. However, Foster cheated. He hyperventilated with oxygen for 30 minutes before entering the water. Foster's longest breath-hold without the benefits of supplementary oxygen is still an amazing five minutes, 40 seconds. We strongly advise against anyone attempting to challenge either of Foster's records!

Most humans wishing to spend extended periods of time under water and do more than just lie on the bottom of swimming pools overcome the problems of breath-holding by taking an air supply down with them, usually in SCUBA tanks (SCUBA is the acronym for Self-Contained Underwater Breathing Apparatus). This approach is not without its own set of problems as we will discuss shortly.

One question that has concerned scientists for decades is how marine mammals have been able to extend the length of time they can hold their breath. Unlike Mr. Foster, they do not require supplementary oxygen and, unlike SCUBA divers, they do not require tanks of compressed air, while actively swimming, searching for food and doing all the other things that they do under water.

When mammals dive, they must rely on oxygen brought from the surface. This oxygen is either held in air in their lungs, carried in their red blood cells or stored in muscle tissues for future use. When these stores are used up, mammals must surface to breathe air in order to replenish their tissues with oxygen and unload the carbon dioxide which accumulates as a by-product of respiration; they must do this to avoid asphyxiation.

If a mammal wishes to increase the length of time it can hold its breath and remain submerged, a number of options are available. It can increase the amount of oxygen stored in its tissues; it can ration the limited oxygen so that only those tissues with the greatest need receive a constant supply; it can slow down the rate at which oxygen stores are depleted during breath-holding or diving; and it can develop methods to make more efficient use of the available oxygen.

Alternatively, a mammal might increase its breath-holding abilities. It could do this by switching from an oxygen-based metabolism (**aerobic** metabolism) to one that does not depend on oxygen (**anaerobic** metabolism). At the same time, it could become more tolerant to the

Dive times recorded for various pinnipeds

Species	Average dive duration (minutes)	Maximum dive duration (minutes)
northern fur seal	2.2	7.6
Galapagos fur seal	less than 2.0	5.0
Antarctic fur seal	less than 2.0	4.9
South African fur seal	2.1	7.5
South American fur seal	2.5	7.1
California sea lion	–	8.0
Galapagos sea lion	less than 2.0	6.0
walrus	–	10.0
harbour seal	less than 5.0	28.0
grey seal	–.	23.0
ringed seal	–	17.0
harp seal	4.5	15.8
hooded seal	–	18.0
northern elephant seal	19.2	47.7
Weddell seal	10.0	73.0

build-up of carbon dioxide and other by-products of metabolism in the blood stream and other body tissues that occurs when an animal holds its breath. Diving birds and mammals use all these 'tricks' to some extent to increase the length of time they can hold their breath while diving.

The pinnipeds have increased the oxygen carrying capacity of their blood to more than three times that of humans. They have accomplished this by having a relatively larger volume of blood, a relatively larger number of small red blood cells and a larger amount of haemoglobin. Haemoglobin is the protein in red blood cells that gives blood its characteristic colour. More importantly, it is the substance that carries the oxygen in the blood and delivers it to the tissues.

Pinnipeds have also increased the capacity of their muscles to store oxygen, by having a higher concentration of another oxygen-binding protein – myoglobin – than is found in terrestrial mammals. Myoglobin concentrations in seal muscles are ten times those found in humans. It is the large amount of myoglobin that gives seal muscle its very dark, almost black, colour.

Diving seals also carefully ration the amount of oxygen delivered to various parts of the body. They constrict the arteries carrying blood to the outer parts of the body and to certain tissues, so that the limited supplies of oxygen are sent only to those tissues most in need, such as the brain and heart. Furthermore, at least some marine mammals seem capable of using their precious oxygen stores more completely than other mammals.

Recent research on Weddell seals suggests that the spleen plays a role in rationing oxygen during a dive, functioning somewhat like a SCUBA tank. A large quantity of oxygenated red blood cells is stored in the spleen prior to diving. During a dive, the seal gradually injects these cells into the blood stream so that during the first ten to 15 minutes of a dive the oxygen content of the blood is maintained at a constant level.

Together, the increased oxygen stores and the selective redistribution of the blood are sufficient to meet the body's needs during short dives. Long dives, however, require further adjustments.

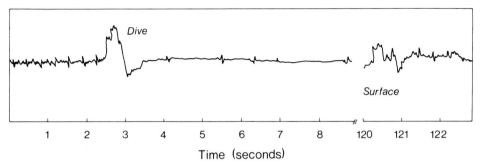

Time (seconds)

Electrocardiogram of a diving seal. As the seal dives, there is a dramatic drop in its heart rate – bradycardia.

During long dives, seals further restrict blood flow to all non-essential parts of the body and circulate blood only between the heart, brain and lungs. They can also slow their heart rates to as low as five or six beats per minute – a phenomenon known as **bradycardia**. These adjustments further reduce the rate at which the limited oxygen supplies are used up during a dive while normal blood pressure is maintained in the essential tissues that require a continuous supply of oxygen. For example, to prevent brain damage, blood pressure to the brain is continuously monitored and carefully controlled by the **autonomic nervous system**. Similarly, in pregnant females, blood flow to the placenta is maintained to ensure that the developing foetus has a constant supply of oxygen.

At the same time, other organs and tissues in the diving seal function at a lower metabolic rate, thereby reducing oxygen consumption. Some tissues are also able to tolerate the build up of metabolic by-products, such as carbon dioxide and lactic acid, which are so debilitating in exercising humans who are 'short of breath'. During extremely long dives, seals can function anaerobically for limited periods of time.

When pinnipeds surface after a dive, they seem able to replenish their oxygen stores and unload accumulated carbon dioxide more efficiently than terrestrial mammals. For example, whereas humans extract about 20 per cent of the oxygen in the air they inhale, the pinnipeds that have been studied appear to be able to remove as much as 34 per cent from each breath of air. Some whales do even better, removing up to 48 per cent.

Much of the early research on diving in pinnipeds was conducted on restrained animals in the laboratory.

From these forced dives, it appeared that diving in pinnipeds could only be explained if animals became anaerobic and accumulated an 'oxygen debt' which could only be 'repaid' when the animal surfaced to breathe. Very recent research on less stressed, freely diving seals now suggests that much of the early research on forced dives was not entirely applicable to animals in nature. Many of the observations arose because animals were restrained and frightened and had no control over the duration of their dives. It would now appear that during most dives, pinnipeds do not exceed their 'aerobic dive limit'. In other words, the duration of most of their dives depends on the amount of oxygen stored in the body and the rate at which the animals use it. And the marked difference between average and maximum dive times in the Table on p. 69 indicates that pinnipeds are usually content to keep their dive times well within the limit imposed by the availability of oxygen. It is only during the relatively rare, extended dives that unrestrained seals exhibit the series of responses observed in restrained animals.

In addition to the oxygen problem, diving mammals have other obstacles to overcome. For human divers water pressure presents the most serious problem. At sea level, atmospheric pressure is equivalent to 760 mm of mercury (101 kilopascals, 10,332 kilograms per square meter, 2,116 pounds per square foot), defined by convention as 1 atmosphere of pressure. When animals dive, pressure increases rapidly: for every ten meters (33 feet) the pressure increases by an additional atmosphere.

There are several ways in which pressure affects human divers. The first is compression. Because most tissues contain water that is incompressible, the increasing pressure encountered with increasing depth has little effect on most organs. There are, however, several parts of the human body, especially the ears, lungs and sinuses, which have air spaces, spaces which are compressible and which hence become smaller as the pressure increases. At a depth of only about 30 meters (100 feet), the pressure is so great that the lungs are compressed to only 25 per cent of their original volume. If this pressure cannot be equilibrated from within, intense pain and even the rupture of tissues may occur.

For humans, diving with the assistance of SCUBA gear and breathing compressed air, there are additional effects of pressure to consider. Under pressure, large amounts of nitrogen, which makes up about 78 per cent of air, become dissolved in the blood and other body fluids. At high concentrations, nitrogen has an anaesthetic effect on the nervous system resulting in a condition known as nitrogen narcosis or rapture of the deep, an affliction similar to intoxication. Ultimately, this can lead to very serious consequences including unconsciousness and death.

Even if levels of dissolved nitrogen do not rise high enough to cause nitrogen narcosis, they may cause another problem – the bends. When a diver surfaces too quickly, the dissolved nitrogen in the body may come out of solution, forming gas bubbles. These gas bubbles may occur in the joints causing excruciating pain. More seriously, gas bubbles may appear in the blood where an embolism may result. Embolisms can block the flow of blood to tissues, and in organs such as the lungs, heart or brain, such blockages are usually fatal. The only treatment is immediate recompression followed by carefully controlled decompression. Decompression chambers are, however, rarely available when needed.

Among humans, the most accomplished free-divers, the legendary pearl divers of Japan and Korea, routinely dive only to depths of ten to 25 meters (33-82 feet). Each dive lasts for about 40 to 50 seconds; the divers surface for a 50 to 60 second rest between dives and perform about 50 dives in the morning and another 50 in the afternoon. Because of the relatively shallow depths encountered and because they are not using compressed air, such divers avoid the most serious problems associated with pressure. Their impressive diving statistics nonethless pall in comparison to the diving feats of some pinnipeds.

Until very recently, estimates of maximum diving depths reached by pinnipeds were largely anecdotal, being obtained opportunistically from the catching of animals on fishing lines or by other fishing gear set at known depths. In recent years, much more precise information has been obtained for several pinnipeds using an ingenious device known as a time-depth recorder (or TDR as it is usually called). This instrument, as its name implies, keeps a log of the durations and depths of all dives for a period of up to several weeks while animals are at sea. Since the TDR must be recovered from the animal in order to obtain the diving record, this approach has been limited to use on animals whose behaviour is sufficiently predictable that the recovery of the expensive instrument is virtually certain.

Data obtained from freely diving pinnipeds, through the use of time-depth recorders, have revealed some remarkable and unexpected results. First used in the Antarctic to study diving behaviour of Weddell seals, the TDR divulged diving capabilities that had not been thought possible. Not only could these animals dive for over one hour, but one animal, a large male, reached a depth of 600 meters (1,969 feet)! At the time, this was the deepest dive ever recorded for an untrained or unharpooned marine mammal.

Northern elephant seal carrying a time-depth recorder.
Photo: D. Costa

In recent years, even more spectacular results have been obtained, particularly from observations on northern elephant seals. Females feeding at sea immediately after lactation dive virtually continuously. One adult female, for example, logged 653 dives in her first 11 days at sea! Her average dive lasted 21 minutes and took her to a depth of 333 meters (1,093 feet), after which she spent about three minutes on the surface before diving again. Her deepest dive was 630 meters (2,067 feet), surpassing all previous records for pinnipeds. Records are made to be broken, however, and this record has subsequently been beaten by yet another female elephant seal that reached the incredible depth of 894 meters (2,933 feet) in a recently recorded dive.

Compare this with the *Guiness Book of Records'* entry for the deepest breath-hold dive by a human. A man by the name of Jacques Mayol descended on a sled to 105 meters (344 feet) in 104 seconds and surfaced some 93 seconds later – a feat that was described as 'extremely dangerous'. The record for a SCUBA diver is 133 meters (437 feet), held jointly by John J. Gruener and R. Neal Watson.

To appreciate how much our understanding of pinniped diving behaviour has changed with the advent of the TDR, one has only to consult some of the older seal literature. For example, a 1968 paper, which summarizes diving depths for a number of pinnipeds, gives a value of 20 to 42 meters (66 to 138 feet) for the northern elephant seal. Even a 1981 review quotes a value of 183 meters (600 feet) as the maximum depth attained by this species.

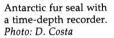

Antarctic fur seal with a time-depth recorder. *Photo: D. Costa*

Diving depths recorded for various pinnipeds

Species	Average dive depth (meters)	(feet)	Maximum dive depth (meters)	(feet)
northern fur seal	68	223	207	679
Galapagos fur seal	26	85	115	377
Antarctic fur seal	30	98	101	331
South African fur seal	45	148	204	669
South American fur seal	34	112	170	558
California sea lion	–	–	250	820
Galapagos sea lion	37	121	186	610
Steller sea lion	–	–	183	600
walrus	–	–	90	295
harbour seal	–	–	200	656
grey seal	–	–	213	699
ringed seal	–	–	90	295
harp seal	–	–	274	899
bearded seal	–	–	200	656
northern elephant seal	400	1,312	894	2,933
Weddell seal	less than 100	<328	600	1,969

Note: Many of these records come from animals carrying time-depth recorders. These are assumed not to affect dramatically the diving behaviour of the seals. All dive depths have been rounded to the nearest meter (or foot).

Other pinnipeds studied with TDRs have not reached the depths recorded by Weddell seals and northern elephant seals but their performances are nonetheless quite impressive (see Table above). Of course, in the majority of their dives, even the Weddell seals and northern elephant seals do not approach the extreme values given above.

Harp and hooded seals seem to be intermediate among phocid seals in their diving abilities. Both species are thought to be capable of diving to about 300 meters (975 feet) but this has yet to be confirmed by precise measurements. Because of their larger size, their preference for off-shore environments and their feeding habits, we suspect that hooded seals routinely dive to deeper depths and, possibly, for longer times, than do harp seals under normal circumstances.

Any SCUBA diver will marvel at the diving accomplishments of pinnipeds, particularly those of the northern
elephant seal. At a depth of almost 900 meters (2,953 feet),
the elephant seal would experience a pressure of 90 atmo-
spheres and, to dive to such depths and to return to the
surface all within about 30 minutes, without tanks of
compressed air and without a decompression chamber and
without running out of oxygen or suffering from the bends
or rapture of the deep, is a remarkable feat.

A hooded seal just
below the surface
retains sufficient air to
inflate its hood.
Photo: R. Frank

Actually, pressure is not a very serious problem for
diving pinnipeds. Their bodies are constructed so that
water pressure has little effect on them. Most of the body
is incompressible while remaining quite flexible. The only
'spaces' occur in the ear and the respiratory tract; there are
no **cranial** sinuses in pinnipeds. Unlike the ears of
humans, the internal ear is well fortified to withstand the
effects of pressure and the middle ear is surrounded by a
layer of tissue that can be filled with blood to equalize the
pressure between the spaces within the ear and the outside
environment. The ribcage and trachea are flexible and
simply become compressed under pressure.

Immediately before diving, seals open their nostrils,
which are normally closed, and exhale the air in their
lungs. This not only reduces the amount of air in the body
but also reduces buoyancy. As the pressure increases, the
soft tissues of the lungs are permitted to collapse
completely without any damage occurring. Any air remaining in the body is confined to the bronchi and bronchioles,
which are reinforced with cartilage to resist compression.
Because these passages are not in contact with the blood

A young harbour seal opens its nostrils to exhale just prior to diving.

stream, air can be safely stored here without any danger that the nitrogen it contains will be absorbed by the body. The heart is also modified slightly, being somewhat broader and flatter than that of a terrestrial mammal to accommodate the reduction in the size of the chest cavity that occurs during a dive.

Because seals do not have large, gas-filled spaces when diving, they apparently do not experience the pain associated with compression. Similarly, since they exhale most of the gas in their lungs before diving deeply, nitrogen is not forced into their body fluids as they descend and the seals run no risk of developing nitrogen narcosis. Consequently, when they rise quickly to the surface there is no nitrogen to form bubbles and cause the bends.

It is clear, then, that the pinnipeds have, through the process of evolution, overcome the difficulties of moving in and under water. They have done so, not through the evolution of unique features, but rather by subtle modifications of the mammalian body plan.

Senses

In order to perceive their new underwater world, marine mammals had to solve some particularly challenging problems. Because mammals evolved on land, their highly developed sense organs evolved to function entirely in air. And once again, the very different nature of air and water required modifications in order for their 'terrestrial' sense organs to function efficiently under water. For the seals, the problems are further compounded: because they spend time on land, they must retain some sensory capabilities in air as well. Here we will briefly describe the modifications in the sense organs of seals that enable them to function in both air and water.

Vision
Seals have very large eyes. The exposed surface, the cornea, protects the delicate, internal parts of the eye. The cornea is constantly lubricated by secretions (tears) produced by lacrimal glands to protect it from salt water, sand or dust. Unlike those of terrestrial mammals, the

Tears.
LEFT: Whitecoat.
RIGHT: Female harp seal.

seals' eyes lack ducts to drain away the tears. For this reason, seals on land or ice frequently appear to be 'crying'. In reality they are not crying; it is simply that the tears have nowhere else to go.

The seals' eyes must function not only in air and in water but also over a wide range of light intensities. For harp and hooded seals, this extends from the blinding brightness of the pack ice on a sunny day to the gloomy darkness encountered during a deep dive.

In air, the typical mammalian eye, exemplified by the human eye, focuses a clear image on a layer of light-sensitive cells – the retina – lining the back of the eyeball. The image is focused by two 'lenses'. The first is the cornea, the clear, outer window of the eye. The second is the lens inside the eye. Together, they focus light on the retina in much the same way that the lens of a camera focuses an image on light-sensitive film. In most people, the eye accomplishes its task quite well and we see images clearly.

If a person with good vision is placed under water, we immediately find that, unaided, the human eye does not function nearly as well as it does in air. This is easily explained. Under water, the cornea effectively 'disappears', just as a glass bead dropped into a glass of water becomes almost invisible. This is because the cornea, a glass bead and water have virtually the same **refractive index**.

The loss of the cornea as a focusing lens under water means that the human eye can no longer bend the light rays sufficiently to focus an image. The result is a condition known as farsightedness (**hypermetropia**). Consequently, humans who suffer from shortsightedness (**myopia**) can, ironically, see more clearly under water than people who have normal vision.

80

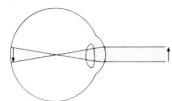

Optics of the human eye in air.

Optics of the human eye under water. The image forms behind the eye resulting in blurred, farsighted vision.

To improve vision under water, swimmers and divers usually wear a mask. Because the faceplate of the mask has a similar refractive index to that of water, it does not directly contribute to the formation of an image on the retina. What it does is restore the layer of air in front of the cornea, enabling the 'terrestrial' eye to function under water with the same two lenses it uses in air. Image quality is dramatically improved, although objects appear about one-third larger and 25 per cent closer than they really are because the light is bent or refracted as it passes from water into air. It is because of differences in the refractive index of air and water that a stick appears to bend as it is inserted into water.

Of course, seals and other mammals (and diving birds) do not have the option of donning a mask when diving under water. Yet, with necessity being the mother of invention even in nature, each has found a means of modifying its eye to improve its functioning under water. Seals and whales have followed the example of fish. To compensate for the 'loss' of the cornea under water, they have evolved large, almost spherical, lenses to increase the

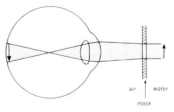

Optics of the human eye, equipped with a mask, under water.

focusing power of their eyes. Thus, a seal in water is capable of seeing a reasonably clear image of its surroundings.

Of course, such a modification of the eye for under-water vision causes the seal new difficulties when on land. In air, with both the cornea and the enlarged lens bending light rays, the pinniped eye becomes shortsighted (i.e. myopic) under some light conditions.

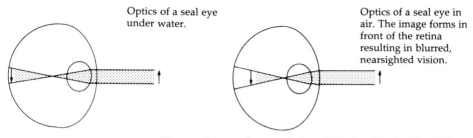

Optics of a seal eye under water.

Optics of a seal eye in air. The image forms in front of the retina resulting in blurred, nearsighted vision.

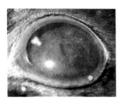

Slit-shaped pupil in a seal eye in bright light.

The problem of myopia is minimized in bright light by the action of the iris diaphragm which controls the size of the pupil – the opening that lets light into the eye. The seal pupil resembles that of the cat. In bright light, it closes down to a narrow vertical slit with a small pinhole at the top. Light entering the eye passes through the pinhole, reducing the ability of the cornea and lens to bend light, thereby minimizing the degree of myopia experienced. Coincidentally, the pinhole pupil will also reduce any blurred vision (i.e. **astigmatism**) that may be caused by the large, curved cornea.

In dim light, the seal pupil, like that of other mammals, dilates to form a wide circle to let in as much of the available light as possible. In so doing, the cornea and most of the lens become involved in the image-forming process. Thus, in dim light, pinnipeds in air are myopic. They may also suffer from astigmatism.

In summary, seals in bright light have relatively good vision in both air and under water. Their ability to perceive fine detail – visual acuity – is perhaps not as refined as that of humans but is nearly as good as that of cats. On land, as

Dilated pupil in air.

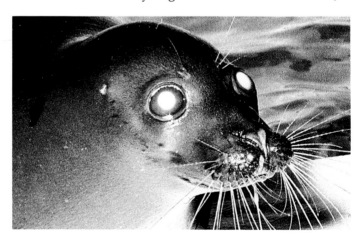

the sun goes down, their visual capabilities decline and in very dim light seals cannot see anything very clearly.

Besides the problems of focusing a clear image on the retina, there is another aspect of vision that is important for mammals that live in dimly-lit environments. Marine mammals require increased visual sensitivity in order to use their eyes when diving to great depths. This is because most of the incident sunlight is reflected, absorbed or scattered in the uppermost layers of the sea, with the result that most of the seals' underwater environment is poorly lit, even on bright, sunny days. Water also acts as a selective filter that limits the penetration of certain colours (wavelengths) of light that make up sunlight. The end result is that the seals' underwater environment, like that of fish, is coloured green or blue, depending on whether the species in question is in coastal waters or polar seas, or farther offshore in the open ocean.

As darkness falls, the ability of a seal to see fine detail (its visual acuity) declines more slowly under water than in air. Seals on land in dim light or darkness are quite myopic.

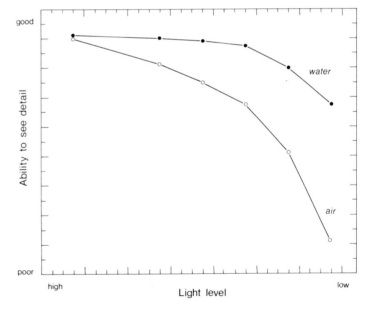

The pinnipeds have dealt with these particular problems in a manner similar to that adopted by nocturnal mammals and fish. They have increased the sensitivity of their eyes by having retinas that contain a large number of very sensitive cells known as rods – the same type that humans use at night. Rod **photoreceptors** provide

The green, underwater world of the harp seal.
Photo: W. Curtsinger – IFAW

increased visual sensitivity at the expense of acuity and the perception of colour (you cannot read easily in very dim light and, as the sun sets, your ability to distinguish different colours is gradually lost).

During the day and in bright artificial light, humans use a second type of photoreceptor known as cones (both photoreceptors get their name from their appearance under a microscope). Although not as sensitive as rods, the cones provide good visual acuity and colour vision.

Seals have retained a small number of cones for vision in bright light, such as that which occurs on the ice fields off eastern Canada. Consistently, there is some evidence that seals, like a number of other carnivores, are capable of limited colour vision.

To further increase the sensitivity of their eyes, seals also have a reflective layer behind the retina, called a tapetum. Light passing through the retina strikes the tapetum and is reflected back so that it has two chances to be detected by the photoreceptors. The tapetum is not unique to seals. It is this structure that is responsible for the 'eyeshine' seen at night when the headlights of a car strike the eyes of various carnivores, including cats and dogs.

Seal (and whale) eyes also appear to be most sensitive to wavelengths of light normally encountered in their marine environment, a trait that they share with fish. Thus, coastal water seals and those such as harp seals and Weddell seals, which are confined to green polar or

'Eyeshine' from a seal's tapetum under water.
Photo: K. Ronald

subpolar seas, have visual pigments in their rods that are most sensitive to green light. Deep diving seals such as the southern elephant seals, which inhabit the bluer waters of the open ocean, have blue-sensitive visual pigments like those found in deep-sea fishes.

In addition to the adaptations described above, seals that breed on pack ice and snow also have corneas that can tolerate the high levels of ultraviolet radiation found in such environments. While these ultraviolet rays enable us to get a sun-tan on the ski-slopes or while observing breeding harp seals on the ice in the Gulf of St. Lawrence, there are some drawbacks. Ultraviolet rays also cause damage to the cornea of the eye and may produce a condition known as snow-blindness. Lacking the tolerant corneas of the seals, tourists should wear sunglasses at all times while on the ice observing seals. Even on cloudy days, there are usually enough ultraviolet rays to irritate the sensitive human cornea.

For seals, vision is probably the most important source of information about their external world. And since seals depend on the aquatic environment for their food, natural selection has placed a high premium on the evolution of a visual system finely tuned to function in water while also retaining the ability to function reasonably well under most conditions encountered on land or ice. Nonetheless, healthy blind seals are occasionally seen in the wild. They are often adult females with pups. How they cope successfully with their handicap is not entirely clear.

Hearing

Just as an eye that evolved for vision in air does not function very well under water without modification, the terrestrial mammalian ear is not entirely appropriate for hearing in water. To appreciate the problems, we will briefly consider how our own ears function in air and water, and then see how the ears of the pinnipeds have been modified to function in both media.

The human ear is sensitive to sound vibrations ranging from about 20 to 20,000 Hertz (cycles per second). With advancing age, most of us will lose our hearing ability above about 12,000 Hertz and will not, therefore, be able to fully appreciate the sound production of our expensive stereos. Although we typically refer to frequencies beyond the limits of the human ear as 'ultrasonics', it would be more honest to admit that our ears are only capable of hearing rather low frequency sounds. The 'silent' whistles we use to call dogs make sounds at frequencies above the capabilities of the human ear but well within the hearing range not only of dogs, but of most mammals, including pinnipeds.

Within our hearing limits, we not only can detect sounds, but we can usually pinpoint their source quite precisely. Such directional hearing is accomplished by having two ears, each equipped with a sound funnel, the external ear or pinna, that directs airborne sounds down the auditory canal to the ear drum, the bones of the middle ear and ultimately to the organ of hearing, the cochlea, housed in the inner ear. Because the ears are on either side of the skull, sounds do not reach each ear at precisely the same time or intensity; this allows the brain to determine the source of the sound.

Although our ears serve us well on land, they do not work nearly as well under water. Only very low frequency sounds reach the ear and these are not heard precisely; nor is it possible to determine accurately the direction of any particular sound. Consequently, SCUBA divers must resort to hand signals, writing slates or line-pull signals to communicate with each other under water.

There are several reasons why the human ear does not function well under water. First, sound waves no longer enter the ear via the air-filled auditory canal. Rather, sound waves travelling through the dense water are transmitted through the bones of the skull and reach the inner ear from all directions; hence the distortion of sound and the loss of directional hearing under water.

In contrast to the performance of the human ear, the pinniped ear actually works better in water than in air. In air, the pinnipeds' hearing range is similar to that of humans, although their hearing is not quite as sensitive. The lack of a large pinna in pinnipeds and the presence of a long ear-canal partially plugged with wax may reduce their hearing capacity in air. Consequently, the hearing of pinnipeds in air is inferior to that of most terrestrial carnivores but it is still quite functional.

Under water, the hearing range of pinnipeds is not only extended to more than 60,000 Hertz but, over those frequencies heard in both air and water, the seal's ear actually hears better under water. Even more remarkable, the seals possess good directional hearing both in air and under water. How the pinnipeds hear so well in both air and water is not entirely understood.

Several modifications of the terrestrial mammalian ear appear to have enhanced their underwater hearing abilities. Structural changes in the inner ear serve to amplify sound reception. Importantly for directional hearing, the bone housing the inner ear, the petrosal, is isolated from all but one of the other bones of the skull. This markedly reduces the amount of sound that can reach the inner ear through the bones of the skull. Modifications of the temporal bone in the seal's skull also serve to accentuate the directionality of the sensations reaching the ear. Unlike the human condition, the seals' ears, therefore, always remain effectively separated on either side of the head permitting good directional hearing under water.

Seals also have specialized tissues lining the auditory canal and the middle-ear cavity that automatically adjust the pressure within the ear when the animal dives. Additionally, evolutionary changes in the relative size of the internal parts of the ear prevent its overstimulation in water where sound travels five times faster than it does in air.

Echolocation

The possession of 'high frequency' hearing in pinnipeds and observations that the vocal repertoire of some species includes pulsed clicks has led a number of biologists to conclude that seals, like some whales and bats, use echolocation or SONAR as an additional source of sensory information about their environment.

Echolocating animals typically send out pulsed sounds that bounce off objects in their path. Detailed information about these objects is provided by the characteristics of the sound waves (or echoes) reflected back to the ears.

Although the ability to echolocate would seem to be useful for seals swimming in murky waters or hunting fish in the dark, there is, however, no good evidence that pinnipeds are able to process and use acoustic echoes for underwater navigation.

Vibrissae

Pinnipeds have well developed whiskers called vibrissae. They are arranged in horizontal rows along both sides of the snout and they vary in number and form among species. Some phocids, like harp and hooded seals, grey seals, ringed seals, harbour (or common) seals and elephant seals, have whiskers that are 'beaded' in structure. The vibrissae of several other pinnipeds, including the northern fur seal, walrus, monk seal and bearded seal, lack the beads and are smooth like those of cats and dogs.

Since the seals' vibrissae are well supplied with nerves, blood vessels and muscles, they seem well equipped to provide sensory information about the external world. Their precise function (or functions), however, is actually not well understood.

There is some evidence that the seals' vibrissae provide tactile information in the same way as do the vibrissae of cats and rats. For example, the vibrissae seem to aid ice-breeding seals in locating the circular holes they use to obtain access to the surface of the ice. On land or ice, the vibrissae are also used to investigate objects or other animals.

Vibrissae.

The vibrissae are also sensitive to low frequency, waterborne vibrations and may function to detect the movement of fish or other aquatic organisms, especially when visibility is poor and the seals are unable to hunt by sight. Under water, they may also help the seal to judge speed.

The vibrissae are also used as communication devices, serving to express a variety of emotions. For example, they are frequently pulled forward and held erect during aggressive encounters as part of a threat posture.

Since there is considerable variation in the length, diameter and surface structure of pinniped vibrissae and in the angles at which they protrude from the nose, there may be some functional differences among pinniped species in the kinds of information the vibrissae provide.

Threatening female harp seal with erect vibrissae.

Smell

The regions of the seal's brain that are responsible for the sense of smell (the olfactory lobes) are small. Nonetheless, odours remain important in the social life of pinnipeds. As we have already seen, harp seal mothers, like many other seal mothers, recognize their offspring primarily through smell, and male fur seals and sea lions use odour to determine the reproductive condition of females. It is quite likely that smell fulfills other social functions as well.

When on land or ice, pinnipeds use smell to detect potential predators. Innuit hunters, for example, are careful to approach seals from down wind as they move in for a kill.

In water, seals keep their nostrils tightly closed, for obvious reasons, and the sense of smell ceases to function.

Feeding adaptations

Since one of the principal benefits for early pinnipeds invading the sea was the presence of a rich and bountiful supply of food, it is not surprising that they now exhibit a number of adaptations that permit them to exploit this resource more effectively.

The most obvious adaptation involves the teeth. Pinniped teeth have changed quite dramatically from those of their terrestrial ancestors who used their teeth to capture prey and then to tear and grind the flesh of their victims. Most pinnipeds simply swallow their food whole.

Pinnipeds have fewer teeth than the primitive mammalian number of 44; for example harp seals have 34 teeth and hooded seals have only 30. Their teeth are also quite simple in structure. Their small, pointed incisors and reasonably well developed canine teeth are suitable for gripping their slippery food. The teeth behind the canines (post-canines), the premolars and molars, are quite small and uniform in appearance, with one or more pointed **cusps**, again to hold food rather than to grind and tear it. None of the pinnipeds have the large shearing teeth, called carnassials, that are found in many terrestrial carnivores including cats and dogs.

Hooded seal teeth.
Photo: R. Frank

Any variation in the complexity of the postcanine teeth within the pinnipeds occurs in the cusp pattern. Antarctic crabeater seals, whose diet is comprised largely of shrimp-like invertebrates called krill, have elaborately-cusped teeth that act as sieves to let water escape from the mouth while the seals retain their prey.

Like other mammals, pinnipeds have two sets of teeth during their lifetime. Their 'baby teeth' are , however, incomplete and non-functional. In fact, in phocids, most of the milk teeth are usually resorbed by the time the pup is born and never occur as a complete set of teeth within the mouth. Those teeth that are not entirely resorbed are pushed through the gums by the larger permanent teeth as they erupt.

When a seal pup is born, the gums may be smooth and toothless or tiny cusps may be present, depending on the species. Most otariids are born with all of their permanent teeth erupted while most phocids have a full set of permanent teeth by the time they are a month old. Pups must be able to feed themselves without any parental help shortly after weaning, so it is important that their teeth develop quickly.

An extreme modification of the teeth is seen in the walrus. They have massive canine teeth called tusks that in large males may reach a length of over 30 centimeters (one foot) and weigh more than five kilograms (more than 10 pounds). These serve a variety of functions, most of which have little to do with feeding. Walruses do not use the tusks like a garden hoe to rake through the mud as is usually depicted in the popular literature. The tusks are much more important in a social context. For example, they provide information on age and sex, and are used in aggressive encounters that maintain the complex social

Walrus tusks.
Photo: E.H. Miller

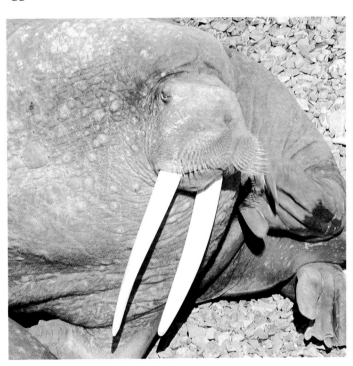

structure of the herd. Individuals may also use their tusks as grappling hooks to help pull themselves up onto ice-floes.

The change in diet from meat to seafood did not necessitate any major modifications in the pinniped digestive system. Consequently, the digestive tract of pinnipeds is relatively simple, like that of terrestrial carnivores. Its most notable characteristic is the length of the small intestine. Whereas the small intestine of a land carnivore may be five or six times the length of the body when unravelled, that of the seal may be as much as 40 times the length of the body, although there is considerable variation, both within and between species. The significance of such a long small intestine in seals is not entirely understood.

Water balance

The typical mammalian body, including that of humans, is about 70 per cent water. In order to maintain this, mammals require a constant supply of fresh water. Because they have difficulty drinking salt water, the marine environment is a virtual desert – 'Water, water everywhere, nor any drop to drink'!

Unlike seabirds, which have special glands for getting rid of excess salt, mammals must make do with their kidneys and there are limits to the amount of salt the mammalian kidney can process. Generally, excessive consumption of sea water causes stomach disorders and because the excretion of salt in urine requires water, drinking salt water actually results in a net loss of body water that, if prolonged, can lead to death. For these reasons, salt water usually acts as an effective barrier to the dispersal of mammals.

Most seals usually avoid the problem entirely simply by not drinking salt water. Even when feeding under water, muscles in the throat prevent all but the smallest amounts of sea water from entering the body. Without a ready source of fresh water, seals normally obtain all of the water they require from the food they eat. The exceptions seem to be otariid seals that may drink salt water when fasting for extended periods in relatively warm environments.

If it is available, seals will occasionally drink fresh water or eat snow, but they rarely need to because their kidneys are extremely efficient. They have the ability to produce a very concentrated urine and therefore, little body water is lost when getting rid of wastes.

Reproductive strategies

The modifications that pinnipeds underwent for thermoregulation and locomotion in water left them somewhat handicapped on solid substrates. Their lack of mobility on land or ice makes them potentially vulnerable to terrestrial predators. It is probably one of the main reasons that pinnipeds choose remote islands and rugged, deserted coastlines, or ice, upon which to give birth and nurse their young. Furthermore, since many pinnipeds spend much of the year widely dispersed while feeding at sea, it behooves them to follow a rigid annual calendar and to have the same breeding sites year after year so that all members of the breeding population can gather to reproduce.

Australian fur seals on breeding beach at Seal Rocks, Australia.
Photo: E.H. Miller

Indeed, most seal species congregate during well defined breeding seasons at traditional sites. Some pack together in extremely dense groupings while others form loose aggregations. Land breeding seals tend to tolerate greater densities than do ice-breeders.

The annual cycle is most rigid and the breeding season most compressed in ice-breeding phocid seals such as harp and hooded seals. Extreme precision is imperative for pack-ice breeders because the ice is only available for a matter of weeks. Tropical species tend to be more flexible in the timing of their reproduction and in some land breeding species, pupping occurs over much of the year.

Grey seal breeding colony on the Isle of May, Scotland.

The three families of pinnipeds each exhibit quite different reproductive strategies. Fur seals and sea lions breed on land in harem groups. Females come ashore just prior to giving birth and join a group of females associated with a large harem bull. After giving birth, females remain with their pups for about a week. Toward the end of the first week of lactation, they come into breeding condition (**estrous**) and copulate with the attending male. Shortly thereafter, they leave their pups and go to sea to feed. Unlike the true seals, which terminate nursing prior to or

94

Large adult South
American sea lion
courts a female in his
harem. Note the large
size difference between
the sexes.
Photo: E.H. Miller

very shortly after mating, female otariids continue to nurse
their young for three to 12 months or more, depending on
the species. They follow a regular cycle of going to the sea
to feed for a week or more and then returning to nurse
their pups and rest for several days before going to the sea
once more.

Otariid pups are quite well developed at birth, being
fully haired with their eyes open and being capable of
crawling around almost immediately. Growth is, however,
quite slow, averaging less than 100 grams (0.63 ounces) per
day.

The true seals, whether they breed on land or ice, all
have much shorter periods of maternal care than otariids
(for example, see pp. 37 and 50). Females give birth to a

Newborn otariid; a
New Zealand fur seal
pup.
Photo: E.H. Miller

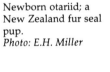

Newborn phocid; a harbour or common seal.

single offspring that, for mother's size, weighs as much as the entire litter produced by many mammalian species.

Like the otariids, true seal pups are born fully haired with their eyes open. They can also move in a reasonably coordinated fashion very shortly after birth. Unlike female fur seals and sea lions, female true seals do not eat while feeding their young; they produce all of the fat-rich milk fed to their pups using only their body reserves. The large body size of female phocids and their large stores of blubber permit such a period of fasting. As a result, phocid pups grow much more quickly than young otariids during the nursing period, usually averaging an increase of over two kilograms (four pounds) per day. During this time, the pups accumulate sufficient energy reserves to nourish them during their first few weeks of independence after weaning.

The rapid development of phocid neonates shortens the period of potential danger for both the female and her pup. It also reduces the 'overhead' costs to the female for maintenance during the nursing period when she is fasting and as we noted earlier for harps and hoods, it permits several species of seals to use the transient pack-ice environment for whelping and nursing.

The breeding systems of adult phocids are more variable and often quite different from that exhibited by the otariids. The 'arrangements' of males and females vary according to species. Some, like the harp seal, are believed to breed promiscuously. Among others, males breed with several females each year, as is likely the case for hooded seals. Some land-breeding species, such as the northern elephant seal, have harems reminiscent of those observed among the otariids. Still others are intermediate, having a system that is not a true harem, but with individual males limiting the access of other males to an area where females tend to congregate. Grey seals are an example of one such species. Males breed with several females and fight to remain within a concentration of cows. They do not, however, restrict the movements of females to or from the area nor do they defend strict territorial boundaries.

Walruses more closely resemble the pattern observed in otariid seals but have a more extended nursing period. In fact, walrus calves are fed and intensively cared for by their mothers for two years or more. As a result, female walruses can give birth only once every two or three years.

The extended period of neonatal dependence in walruses is thought to be due to their specialized mode of feeding. They eat molluscs, shellfish that they vacuum from the ocean floor. They then suck the fleshy body out

Walrus calf with mom and friends.
Photo: E.H. Miller

of its shell. This means that in order to survive without mother's milk, walrus calves must be able to dive to the bottom, remain there long enough to search for food, find food and then be powerful enough to suck the food from its shell. To become accomplished at these tasks takes time!

From this overview, we can see that seals have overcome many of the difficulties associated with life in water, while maintaining some abilities to function on land or ice. It is ironic that several of these adaptations, such as their fidelity to specific breeding sites, the fur coats of fur seals and sea lions, the blubber and coats of true seals, and the tough skin, blubber and tusks of walruses, which have allowed them to survive and prosper for millions of years in the marine environment, are the very traits that have made pinnipeds the target of exploitation by humans.

In some cases, overexploitation took the seals to the brink of extinction or beyond. In the next chapter, we will review one of the important 'theatres' in *'The War Against the Seals'*, the centuries-old hunt for harp and hooded seals in the north Atlantic – once called *'The Greatest Hunt in the World'*.

A walrus surfaces after a dive. It appears ghostly white because it has restricted blood flow to the skin to conserve heat while in the cold water.
Photo: E.H. Miller

A two-day old harbour seal goes for a swim.

S.S. Imogene leaving for the Icefields. Original Etching by David Blackwood. 20 x 32 inches, 1973.

5. History of the Northwest Atlantic Seal Hunt

For as long as humans have lived in coastal marine communities they have depended on the 'resources' of the sea for their existence. In parts of the world, particularly in northern regions, marine mammals, including seals, have provided many of the necessities of life – food, fuel for heat and light, clothing, equipment and shelter. It is not surprising then that abundant harp seals, and to a limited extent, hooded seals, played a significant role in the settlement of west Greenland and the east coast of Canada through much of recorded history.

When European explorers first set foot in the New World, seal hunting was a well established practice among the aboriginal peoples in what is today Atlantic Canada. This is well documented in the diaries and logs of John Cabot (1497), Jacques Cartier (1534) and Samuel de Champlain (1632).

Archaeological evidence indicates that the use of seals by the indigenous peoples of eastern North America dates back at least 4000 years, to the Archaic Indians who lived along the west coast of the Great Northern Peninsula of the island of Newfoundland. Later, Dorset Eskimos in the same region relied heavily on seals and other marine mammals for their survival. In southern Greenland, seals, including both harp and hooded seals, played a vital role in the establishment of Norse settlements as early as 985 AD. It has been suggested that competition with the resident Innuit for harp seals may have even played a role in the decline and eventual extinction of these settlements by about 1500 AD.

The first European sealers

Almost immediately upon their arrival in the New World, the Europeans began to exploit the bountiful resources of the northwest Atlantic – fish, whales, seals and seabirds. Although one associates modern seal hunting in eastern Canada with harp and hooded seals, this was not always the case. Initially, early sealers took advantage of other pinnipeds that gathered in large numbers on islands and along the coasts, the ones that were most accessible and the easiest to slaughter.

The first victims were the walruses (also known then as sea cows, sea oxen, sea horses or morse) that congregated to breed along the eastern seaboard of North America south to Cape Cod, on Sable Island (then known as Santa Cruz) off present-day Nova Scotia, and throughout the Gulf of St. Lawrence, including Prince Edward Island (originally Ile Saint-Jean), the Magdalen Islands, St. Pierre et Miquelon, and Newfoundland. Beginning early in the 16th century, a succession of Portuguese and French merchants, Spanish Basques, British colonists, and displaced Acadians unmercifully and relentlessly exploited the walrus primarily for its valuable '**train**' oil, ivory tusks and leather.

Slaughtering sea horses in the 19th century. *From a print engraved by George Cooke, dated 1 December 1811, and published by Longman, Hurst, Rees, Orme & Brown, London*

The decimation of these southern walrus populations was quick, complete and permanent. All walruses along the St. Lawrence River had disappeared by 1680 and those along the North Shore of the Gulf by 1704. By 1710, the large population on Sable Island was no more. In Massachusetts, the last walrus, possibly a straggler from farther north, was killed in 1754. In the Gulf of St. Lawrence, the last individual was sighted off the Magdalen Islands in 1800. It was not until 1987, however, that the St. Lawrence walrus population was officially declared 'extirpated' by the Committee on the Status of Endangered Wildlife in Canada.

In addition to the walrus, the early explorers also found large numbers of grey seals and harbour seals along the northeastern coast of North America, throughout the Gulf of St. Lawrence and penetrating the length of the St. Lawrence River. A population of harbour seals even reached the fresh waters of Lake Ontario.

For a time, the larger grey seal, or horsehead as it is often called even today, became one of the principal exploitable resources in the New World. As with the walrus, the grey seals were slaughtered by the thousands, from New England to Newfoundland. And as the walrus became depleted, the grey seal, although somewhat smaller, was a convenient and acceptable substitute, supplying vast quantities of valuable oil. By 1790, for

Male grey seal or 'horsehead'.

example, a year-round grey seal hunt had become a lucrative occupation on the Magdalen Islands.

Not surprisingly, by the 1860s, the grey seal had been wiped out over much of its former range. The remaining animals were so few in number and so scattered that they could no longer support a sealing industry. The species eventually faded from view. So reduced were its numbers that as recently as the late 1940s, the grey seal was thought to be extinct in eastern Canada.

Because of their smaller size, low oil yield and scattered distribution, the harbour seals escaped major commercial exploitation. Nonetheless, human settlements encroached on their habitats and they were hunted by settlers along the coast for food, household oil, and leather for boots and clothing. Of course, when oil prices were high, there was considerable motivation for fishermen and small-scale sealers to hunt harbour seals, especially in places such as Sable Island where they could be massacred in large numbers. In the short term, such intensive hunts greatly reduced the number of harbour seals locally. Nonetheless, they survive today, scattered over much of their former range, albeit in rather small numbers. An obvious exception is the harbour seal population that once inhabited Lake Ontario, the last member of which was apparently killed in 1824.

Harbour seals.

It was only a matter of time before the vast herds of ice-breeding seals, the harps and hoods, were discovered. The annual hunt for these two species eventually became the largest and most enduring of any seal hunt anywhere in the world. Of course, it was this hunt that captured world interest and became an annual media event over 20 years ago. Its principal quarry, the white-coated pup of the harp seal, became the symbol for all exploited animals.

Although the harp and hooded seals together greatly outnumbered the other pinnipeds in the New World, they were not immediately noticed by the early explorers and entrepreneurs because they were only present during the winter. Even then, they remained in the water or on the inhospitable ice offshore and were seldom seen.

The roots of the annual hunt for harp and hooded seals can be traced back to the 16th and early 17th century when Spanish Basque whalers first hunted walruses and seals in the Gulf of St. Lawrence and off the coast of Labrador.

By the mid-17th century, French settlers were hunting the harp seals that gathered to feed in the St. Lawrence River in the winter months prior to the breeding season. Initially, animals were shot from small boats. This was a very inefficient way to hunt harp seals but it was not long before the settlers adopted the methods of the local Innuit, who at that time wintered as far south and west as Anticosti Island. Lacking guns, the Innuit used nets made of sealskin to catch the seals.

Soon, the French established a net 'fishery' for seals along the North Shore of the St. Lawrence River. New settlements or 'seigneuries' were established to take advantage of this new fishery and by 1700, these extended along the St. Lawrence, as far east as the Mingan Islands. By 1689, other seigneuries had been established on the northwest coast of Newfoundland to exploit harp seals as they migrated through the Strait of Belle Isle on their way south to the Gulf and the St. Lawrence River estuary.

The land-based net fishery was so lucrative that by 1720, having displaced the Innuit from the entire North Shore, the French extended the string of seigneuries from Tadoussac, along the North Shore to Belle Isle, and up the Labrador coast to Hamilton Inlet. Additional sealing stations were established along the west coast of Newfoundland.

With the expansion of settlements, technological advancements in net design and complexity, and an increased knowledge of the biology of the seals gained through experience, the number of seals taken each year increased. By the mid-18th century, New France was exporting 500 tons of seal oil each year, equivalent to an annual kill of at least 6,000 adult seals. Of course, this would be over and above the oil used by the settlers. No records of the total kill seem to have survived.

The beginnings of the Newfoundland seal hunt

English settlers, living in French-claimed territory on the northeast coast of Newfoundland, also began sealing in the early 18th century. Initially, summer fishing crews were left on the Island to overwinter and to hunt harp seals when they arrived in the south. As in other locales, the presence of seals during the winter provided the economic incentives that led to the establishment of permanent settlements to 'prosecute' the cod fishery in summer and the seal fishery in winter.

The use of the word *fishery* to describe a seal hunt may at first seem strange but it has a long tradition and even today responsibility for the management of seals in Canadian waters rests with the Department of *Fisheries and Oceans*. George Allen England, writing in 1924, provides a possible explanation. He noted that the 'Church in Newfoundland has ruled that seals are fish, so that even the most pious Newfoundlander can eat seal meat on Friday or during Lent'. Perhaps as a consequence, England found that 'Newfoundlanders insist that seals are fish!'

Following the lead of the French, the early English sealers fished for harp seals with nets from shore. Over the years, continued improvements in both the design and construction of the sealing net led to the development of a seal trap. Men in boats herded migrating groups of seals into the trap and then elderly men, women and children raised nets to close it. In their efforts to escape, the seals became enmeshed in the nets and died. It remains debatable whether these seals drowned or, as recent evidence would suggest, actually suffocated because their highly-developed diving response prevented them from attempting to breathe while trapped under water.

Remnants of the net fishery still survive today in parts of Newfoundland and along the North Shore of the St. Lawrence River.

Net fishery for harp seals.
Photo: R. Frank

The harvest of migrating adult animals by the net fishery was supplemented by a spring hunt for whitecoats whenever the ice brought the whelping herd within walking distance. The British sealers also discovered that large numbers of young of the year (beaters) and immature harp seals (bedlamers) often frequented bays along the east coast during the spring and, using small boats and guns, they quickly established a new seal hunt for these animals.

As a result of these initiatives, the annual Newfoundland seal hunt was born. Statistics giving the volume of oil manufactured are available for many years, beginning in 1723. Already, the seal hunt was making a significant contribution to the economy of Newfoundland and certainly, by the 1740s, the British were shipping substantial quantities of seal oil back to the Motherland. For example, in the spring of 1742, the two small outport communities of Fogo and Twillingate exported seal oil valued at 12,550 pounds sterling.

Seal oil, like the oil obtained from whales and

seabirds, had many uses. It was used, for example, as fuel for lamps, as lubricating oil and cooking oil. It was also used in the processing of leather and jute and as a constituent in soap.

Based on the available figures for oil exports, annual catches of seals by the British in Newfoundland ranged from about 7,000 to 128,000 animals between 1723 and 1795. Much of the variation in oil production can be explained by variations in the behaviour of the seals, by the vicissitudes of the weather, and no doubt, by conflicts with the French, who still laid claim to fishing rights along much of the Newfoundland coast even after The Treaty of Paris of 1763 gave Britain control over previously-held French territory at the end of the Seven Years' War. Exceptionally large catches were realized in years when the whelping ice was carried inshore and seals became accessible to the local inhabitants. For example, the 1773 catch of almost 128,000 seals included about 50,000 whitecoats that were taken when the whelping ice piled into Notre Dame Bay.

It was not long before the growing maritime population of Newfoundland began to use small vessels to hunt seals. During the latter half of the 18th century, ten to 15 meter (20-40 foot), decked vessels were used to search for seals, particularly for beaters in the spring, beyond walking distance from shore. The men in these small boats, hunting for a day or two at a time near their homes were, and still are, known as 'landsmen'.

It was at the beginning of the nineteeth century that a large-scale commercial fishery for seals began in earnest in Newfoundland. Sailing schooners were used to take men to the ice to hunt seals on the whelping patches. As it had for the early settlers, the winter and early spring seal fishery provided a perfect complement to the summer and fall cod fishery and the potential for 'off-season' income was quickly realized, particularly by the owners and outfitters of the sailing schooners. With only minor modification, such as reinforcing the bow with false beams, such ships could be used for both fisheries rather than lying idle all winter. Very quickly, the schooner fishery for seals surpassed the contribution of the landsmen to the overall growth of the colony. Landed catches between 1803 and

1816 averaged about 117,000 animals per year.

The 1817 hunt was less successful. Fewer than 40,000 seals were landed. That year, a ferocious spring storm apparently hit the whelping patch; at least 25 vessels were reportedly crushed and lost in the ice, and nearly 200 sealers perished in the frigid waters of the north Atlantic. This was one of the early Newfoundland sealing disasters, but it was not the last. Between 1800 and 1865, approximately 400 vessels were lost and 1,000 men perished in the pursuit of 'fat'.

Human tragedy is frequently the stuff of legends. We are constantly reminded of the sinking of the *Titanic* and the devastation of the Great Wars. On a more regional scale, the loss of human life became part of the reality and the legend of the Newfoundland seal hunt, part of a tradition which when examined from afar, in both time and space, seems more tragic than grand.

Seemingly unperturbed by the ever-present dangers, the Newfoundlanders 'prosecuted the seal fishery' with new intensity the following year and for all intents and purposes, 1818 marks the beginning of the Golden Age of Sealing in the northwest Atlantic. More and larger vessels were sent to the ice in search of the main concentrations of whelping harp seals off the coast of Newfoundland and Labrador. And they were well rewarded for their efforts. The landed catch in that year was a new, but short-lived record, exceeding 200,000 seals for the first time. This was only a sign of things to come. The annual catch would fall below this figure in only three seasons between 1819 and the turn of the century.

Early sealing in the Magdalen Islands

Just as the sealing industry was becoming established in Newfoundland, there were other developments in the Magdalen Islands near the other great concentration of whelping harp seals in the northwest Atlantic. These islands had been settled in the latter half of the 18th century by perhaps 200 Acadians who came to the islands in search of a better life for themselves, but in reality found a rather cruel existence under the direction of the

◀The Magdalen Islands▲
in March.

Islands' owner, an American colonel by the name of Richard Gridley. Gridley, a man usually described as a 'Boston tyrant', had fought beside General Wolfe on the Plains of Abraham, and was given deed to the Islands in 1763 by King George III. During his stay, Gridley oversaw the destruction of the walrus herds. He took his profits and departed when their extermination was assured.

The collapse of the walrus hunt freed the Acadians of their feudal overseer. More than half of them left in search of greener pastures. Those who stayed hunted grey seals year-round and harp (and possibly hooded) seals, if they came close to shore in the spring. They fished and worked the land during the summer, raised cattle for meat and sheep for wool and hunted in the forests. They also salvaged the many shipwrecks that came to grief on their shores. (The Magdalen Islands are sometimes known as the 'Graveyard of the Gulf'.)

In 1806, when Gridley gave up his claim to the 'Maggies', a new Governor, Admiral Isaac Coffin, took possession on behalf of the British Crown. Apparently to mark the occasion, Coffin had a commemorative penny struck, depicting the two local 'resources' he intended to exploit – fish and seals. According to legend, the Magdalen Islanders were not particularly enthusiastic about returning to a life of servitude and the coin, dated 1815, was never actually used as currency on the Magdalen Islands. It did apparently enter circulation on the mainland of Lower Canada and it can still be purchased in coin stores today for a modest price.

Coffin's coin.

The history of the seal hunt in the Magdalen Islands is not at all well documented. Like the landsmen of Newfoundland, the Madelinots (as the Magdalen Islanders are called) first hunted seals in those years when the ice brought them close to shore. Later, they used small boats called *canots* that they dragged across the ice to cross 'leads' of open water and to transport the products of their efforts back to shore. Eventually, they also employed small schooners to hunt seals along the ice edge after the pups had been weaned and had entered the water. They also introduced a new method for hunting seals – trawl-lines with large, baited hooks, a particularly gruesome method that remained in practice until it was banned in the early 1960s.

Despite the presence of a major 'whelping patch' off their shores, the Madelinots never did develop their own large-scale sealing operations. The only large vessels hunting seals in the Gulf of St. Lawrence came from elsewhere, first from Newfoundland, later from Nova Scotia, and for a

Modern landsmen's
vessel in the Gulf
during the 1970s.

time after the Second World War, from Norway. Thus, the Magdalen Islands' seal hunt was, and remains, largely a landsmen's hunt and the story of the great east coast seal hunt is essentially the story of the Newfoundland hunt.

Landmen's catch –
mainly whitecoats with
blubber attached. The
sealer is loading the
pail with fore flippers.
Seal-flipper pie is
considered a delicacy
in Newfoundland and
in parts of the
Magdalen Islands.

A modern *canot.*

The Golden Age of Sealing, 1818-1862

The early sealing successes of the decked sailing schooners quickly led to the construction of more boats and the involvement of more men in the Newfoundland seal hunt. Consequently, the seal fishery expanded rapidly and by the middle of the 19th century was second only to the cod fishery in the resource-based economy of the British colony. The seal hunt was securely entrenched for all time in the economy, culture and tradition of Newfoundland.

Each year more men participated, more ships sailed and more seals died. In many years, landed catches exceeded 500,000 seals, with the greatest catches occurring in 1831, 1832 and 1844 when some 680,000, 740,000 and 686,000 seals, respectively, were reportedly killed.

During the entire period of 1818-1862, more than 18.3 million seals were landed by the Newfoundland sealers. This works out to an average of more than 400,000 seals per year over the entire period. Unbelievable as these figures may seem, they actually represent a minimum estimate of the numbers of seals that actually died at the hands of the sealers.

In those days, the sealers routinely collected the seal pelts in a central location on the ice rather than loading them directly onto the ships. Because of inclement weather or drifting ice, many of these pelts, in some years numbering in the tens of thousands, were never recovered and therefore were not reported in the landed catches. Likewise, ships loaded with untold numbers of pelts were occasionally lost or crushed in the ice. Their crews were usually picked up by boats working in the same area and, remarkably, no major disasters occurred during this period.

Most of the seals killed were harp seals, primarily white-coated pups, but the figures also include a number of older harp seals and a small but unknown number of hooded seals. The exact composition of the catch in these early days is not known because the **sculps** – the pelts with blubber attached – were not recorded separately by species until 1895.

All that really mattered was the amount of oil. It did not matter whether it came from a harp seal, a hooded seal or any other kind of seal, as long as the animals were

available in sufficient numbers to make the operation profitable. Even the true identity of the harp seals, killed by
the hundreds of thousands at Newfoundland as well as at
Jan Mayen, was not well established during this period of
intensive sealing. In fact, an 1839 book on seals actually
lists the harp seal as two species, the Harp or Greenland
Seal in the northwest Atlantic off Newfoundland and the
Ocean Seal of Lepechin in the northeast Atlantic.

Harp or Greenland
seal.

*Both illustrations are
from Jardine's Natural-
ist's Library, Volume
VIII. 1839. W.H. Lizars,
London*

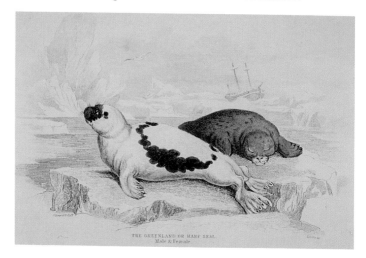

THE GREENLAND OR HARP SEAL.
Male & Female

Oceanic seal of
Lepechin.

THE OCEAN SEAL OF LEPECHIN

'First Cents Issue', 1865. (Note the 5¢ stamp was issued in two colours; forgeries of both were produced in the late 19th and early 20th century to take advantage of unsuspecting stamp collectors.)

Harp seal stamp, 1876.

It was the spring of 1857 that saw both the greatest number of ships sail and the greatest number of men on the ice. Over 370 boats carried 13,600 men to the whelping herds to hunt the seals. Again, more than 500,000 seals, with a landed value of 425,000 pounds sterling, were recorded in the catch statistics. More than 500,000 seals were landed again the following year. But then something happened. Catches began to fall, in 1859 and 1860 to 329,185 and 444,202 seals respectively, and in 1861 and 1862 to 375,282 and 268,624.

Although the industry would continue to be a primary employer in Newfoundland for decades to come, the record catches of the Golden Age of Sealing would seldom be seen again despite continued investment and technological advances. The years of overharvesting had taken their toll and in only two subsequent seasons, 1871 and 1876, did annual catches ever again exceed half a million seals.

The significance of the seal hunt to Newfoundland in the 19th century, and its importance in the tradition and culture of the island are perhaps best symbolized by the presence of harp seals and sealing vessels on the postage stamps of this Dominion (i.e. Newfoundland) of the British Commonwealth shortly after it was granted responsible government in 1855. Although the first stamps issued in 1857, and those produced between 1860 and 1862, all depicted flowers, this changed in 1865 with the appearance of the 'First Cents Issue'. Of the six stamps in this issue, two depicted the visage of the British Monarch, Queen Victoria, one depicted her recently-deceased husband, Prince Albert, while the remaining three depicted a sailing schooner, a cod fish and a harp seal. Of the four stamps issued in 1876-1879, one depicted Queen Victoria, another, her son, The Prince of Wales; the remaining two repeated

Harp seal stamps: 1880   1887   1894

the 1865 images of the cod and the harp seal, although in different colours. A modified harp seal image was included in the issues of 1880, 1887 and 1894. Note that the fore flippers are now held close to the side of the animal. This change apparently arose because of criticisms, not at all justified, about the forward position of the front flippers in the earlier issues.

The wooden-walled steamers, 1863-1943

A new era in Newfoundland sealing dawned in 1862 with the arrival at the sealing grounds of two steam-powered vessels out of Dundee, Scotland. These Scottish steamers had concentrated previously on whaling in the Davis Strait, but had routinely topped-up their catches with seals hunted around the Greenland coast. They were attracted to Newfoundland by the promise of new fortunes.

Although their first season on the ice off Newfoundland was a complete failure, largely because of unfavourable winds, their mere appearance transformed the nature and character of sealing in the British colony for all time. Newfoundlanders instantly recognized the superiority of steam over sail and marvelled at the manoeuverability of the steamers as they rescued the crews of two Newfoundland sailing vessels lost to the ice. Two Newfoundland companies immediately purchased their own wooden-walled steamers in Dundee, in time to go to the Front the following year.

For the second consecutive year, the weather did not cooperate and catches of the steamers were meagre. So disillusioned were the Dundee entrepreneurs that they abandoned, for a time, further trips to the Newfoundland ice. Instead, they renewed their commitment to exploit the sealing grounds at Jan Mayen, off the east coast of Greenland. There they returned annually in full force for more than a decade.

Although the two Newfoundland steamers accounted for only 4,340 of the 387,151 seals landed in 1864, their owners were sufficiently encouraged to press on; one, Baine, Johnson & Co., purchased a second steamer for the next season. And as luck would have it, 1865 was the first truly successful season for the new, steam-powered vessels. The three wooden-walls brought back a catch of over 19,000 seals. Thereafter, the number of steamers increased rapidly.

The small sailing vessels that had been so successful during the Golden Age of Sealing soon found that they could not compete with the larger, steam-driven vessels. Consequently, the number of sailing vessels quickly declined and the number of steamers rapidly increased, to a maximum of 27 by the year 1880.

With the transition from sail to steam, the stakes in the annual seal hunt lottery increased dramatically. The expense involved in acquiring, equipping and operating the steamers was much higher and hence financial losses were much greater in years when sealing was relatively poor. When hundreds of small schooners had sailed with small crews made up of family and friends, the money earned from sealing had made its way throughout the colony. With the advent of the steamers, only the wealthy boat owners, the Water Street merchants from St. John's, could afford to operate the sealing vessels. Large profits became the driving force behind the industry; conditions of employment rapidly deteriorated for the men going to the ice.

Water Street, St. John's, Newfoundland.
Photo: Provincial Archives of Newfoundland & Labrador

The introduction of larger, steam-powered vessels provided some reprieve for the sealing industry, reversing for a time the apparent trend of declining catches that had been observed between 1859 and 1862. Annual catches for the decade of the '60s averaged 320,000, increasing with the number of wooden-walled steamers to 430,000 during the '70s.

Meanwhile, the future of the Newfoundland seal hunt and the populations of seals it exploited were foreshadowed by events at Jan Mayen. The Dundee fleet had managed to deplete the harp seal population there to such low levels that it was becoming unprofitable to send large vessels to the hunt. Given the successes of the Newfoundland fleet, it is not surprising that the Dundee steamers returned to the Front in 1876.

The return of the Dundee vessels was initially met with reservation by local hunters, but large influxes of capital and the use of Newfoundland crews smoothed their integration into the sealing fleet.

During the 1880s the success rate of the Newfoundland sealing fleet began to decline precipitously, as the Greenland ventures had done ten years before. Annual catches declined to 325,000, a drop of more than 100,000, compared with those of the previous decade. Competition for seals became increasingly intense and, in addition to Newfoundland crews, the Scottish companies began to hire on the most experienced Newfoundland ice-masters to captain their ships.

Living conditions on board the sealing boats became abhorrent; the men were underfed, receiving only sea biscuits and tea four or five days a week, and little more on the remaining days. Washing facilities and clean, fresh water were almost non-existent. The men were provided with little or no warm clothing or safety gear. Three or four men had to share a bunk until the pelts were loaded; then the sealers were forced to take their belongings and live on top of the pelts for the final weeks of the hunt.

The sealers were exploited to the fullest by boatowners interested only in the tonnage of oil produced. Even local owners and the Newfoundland captains did little or nothing to improve the lot of their countrymen. Fame and fortune for captains and owners were the top priorities.

Yet, despite seemingly intolerable conditions, men not only continued to sign up to go to the ice, but during the years of the steamers, they actually paid a 'berth' fee for the 'privilege' of participating in the hunt.

In retrospect, it is difficult to understand what made the men return to the dangers of the ice under these conditions. No doubt, the depressed economy of the island and the pride and tradition associated with the annual hunt contributed. Men from all over the island competed for a limited number of positions on the ships and the prospect of sealing continued to attract young men to the ice and, at times, to their deaths.

Blessing the sealing fleet prior to departure from St. John's.
Photo: Provincial Archives of Newfoundland & Labrador

Catches continued to decline, averaging 307,000 for the five years between 1890 and 1895. It was in 1895 that, for the first time, harp and hooded seals were distinguished in the catch statistics: individual prices were paid for young harps, bedlamers, old harps, young hoods and old hoods.

From the first appearance of the wooden-walls in 1863 to the turn of the century, another 12.8 million seals were landed in Newfoundland, bringing the total for the

Sealers from two ships string out over the ice. Each man carries a gaff.
Photo: Provincial Archives of Newfoundland & Labrador

A steamer – the *Terra Nova* – ice-bound in the Narrows, St. John's, Newfoundland.
Photo: Provincial Archives of Newfoundland & Labrador

century to a mind-boggling 33 million animals. This was not accomplished without substantial losses to the wooden-walled fleet.

Of the 50 different Newfoundland steamers that entered the fishery between 1863 and 1895, 36 (72 per cent) were lost, usually crushed in the ice or sunk on their way to and from the killing fields. Those that sank had an average life span of only 16 years and, by 1895, only 16 of the wooden-walls remained active in the seal hunt.

A few of the old wooden-walls survived and went on to greater fame and glory. Between 1907 and 1909, the 41 year old, 300 ton *Nimrod* (in *Genesis*, 'The mighty hunter before the Lord') took British explorer Ernest Shackleton to Antarctica. It was on this expedition that Shackleton

120

achieved a new 'Furthest South', coming within 97 miles of the South Pole.

Perhaps the best known of the wooden-walled sealers was the 700 ton *Terra Nova*. Built in 1884, she participated in 19 consecutive sealing seasons during which time she also served as a relief ship for the 1901-1903 British Discovery Expedition to the Antarctic, led by the legendary Captain Robert Falcon Scott. The *Terra Nova* missed the sealing seasons of 1904 and 1905, but returned for the seasons of 1906-1909. Then she departed again, this time to serve as Scott's ship for the doomed British Antarctic Expedition of 1910-1913. It was during this expedition that Scott achieved his goal, reaching the South Pole – only to find that the Norwegian explorer, Roald Amundsen, had beaten him by a month. Scott and his four companions perished on their return journey in what was later labelled their 'death march in Antarctica'. The *Terra Nova* returned to England without Scott, and was back on the sealing grounds off Newfoundland the following year, 1914. She returned year after year until the Second World War interrupted large vessel sealing in 1941.

Terra Nova in the pack, 1903.
Photo: Provincial Archives of Newfoundland & Labrador

Terra Nova, circa 1935.
*Photo: Provincial
Archives of Newfound-
land & Labrador*

Harp seal stamp, 1897.

The *Terra Nova* would never go to the ice again. On 14 September 1943, off the southwest coast of Greenland, she sprang a leak and sank, but not before her captain and crew had safely abandoned ship. Only her figure-head, a draped female that had been removed in 1913, survives – in the National Museum of Wales.

As the 19th century wound down, the central place of the harp seal in the history and tradition of Newfoundland was appropriately remembered with the inclusion of a seal stamp in the 1897 issue commemorating both the 400th Anniversary of the 'discovery' of the island by John Cabot and the 60th Anniversary of the Reign of Queen Victoria.

The Newfoundland sealing industry continued to tick over between 1895 and 1905; an average of 20 wooden-walled steamers prosecuted the seal hunt annually, landing an average of 279,000 seals each year. Another 48 men died on the ice in the *Greenland* disaster of 1898.

Steel-hulled steamers

It was time to revitalize the industry again. In 1906, the first steel-hulled steamers entered the fishery. These new vessels were more powerful and often larger than the wooden steamers. They were also more expensive to build and operate, and the sealing industry became even more centralized under the control of the Water Street merchants in St. John's. The sealing fleet, now a mixture of old wooden-walls and new steel-hulled ships, almost managed to sustain the catches of the previous decade, landing an average of 266,000 seals per year between 1906 and 1914.

The year 1914 was the year of the 'Great *Newfoundland* Sealing Disaster' so vividly captured in Cassie Brown's book *Death on the Ice*. Brown describes the disaster as one of 'bungling and greed, of suffering and heroism.' The *Halifax Chronicle* described it as 'a story of tragedy and death, of suffering and endurance, of indecision and ruthlessness'.

A.J. Harvey and Company had sent four ships to the ice that year, the oldest of which was the 42-year old wooden-walled steamer, the *S.S. Newfoundland*, with a crew of 189 men, under the direction of Captain Westbury

SEALING STEAMERS AWAITING TO DISCHARGE BOWRING BROS. LTD. ST. JOHNS N.

Steal-hulled steamers.
*Photo: Provincial
Archives of Newfound-
land & Labrador*

Kean. It was a heavy-ice year and the *Newfoundland*
became jammed several kilometers from seals. Not wishing to miss out on the harvest, Wes Kean ordered his men
to set off, on March 31, with instructions that they walk to
their sister ship, the *S.S. Stephano*, captained by his father,
Abram Kean, the greatest sealer of all time. The weather
soon began to close in and, much to the disgust of the
younger Kean, 34 men returned to the *Newfoundland*; the
remainder, however, pushed on and reached the *Stephano*
at 11:20 am. After the men were fed lunch, Abram Kean
put them back on the ice to kill seals, telling them to
return afterwards to their own ship.

Obedient servants, they headed off towards the seals,
torn between Captain Kean's order to kill seals and their
fear of the impending storm. After much indecision and
some bickering, it was mid-afternoon before they began to
head back to the *Newfoundland*.

As the storm raged, Abram Kean was confident the
men had reached his son's ship; Wes Kean was sure the
men had remained aboard the *Stephano*; yet the two men

Abram Kean.
*Photo: Provincial
Archives of Newfound-
land & Labrador*

were prevented from discussing the unfolding disaster because, unlike most sealing ships of the day, the *Newfoundland* did not have a wireless, the owners believing it an unnecessary expense on such an old ship. The men never reached the *Newfoundland*.

Trapped by the blizzard, the men spent two nights and a day on the ice in temperatures as low as -34°C (-30°F) before they were found by another sealing vessel, the *S.S. Bellaventure*. The men of the *Newfoundland* had been dressed for a warm day of killing seals and were ill-equipped to survive in such a blizzard. It is said that some were driven insane and walked off into the sea; some attempted to keep moving to stay awake and died on their feet, frozen as statues; a man and his two sons perished with their arms wrapped around each other. In all, 77 sealers were dead; a 78th died in hospital and many of the survivors later lost limbs to frostbite.

Two judicial enquiries subsequently investigated the *Newfoundland* disaster. Public opinion placed the blame squarely on Abram Kean but he was never officially held responsible. Two Commissioners involved in the second investigation, a Public Commission of Enquiry, decided that Captain Kean 'had made a grave error of judgement'; the third Commissioner filed a judgement without apportioning blame, describing the disaster as an 'act of God'.

In 1915, a petition of 3,000 names demanded that Captain Abram Kean be arrested and charged with criminal negligence in the death of the 78 men. Kean was never charged. Instead, he was awarded $500, later reduced to $100, in a defamation suit against the *Mail and Advocate*, the newspaper that had published the petition. Not a single cent of damages or other liability was ever assessed against the shipowners or the captain.

The two ships involved in the 1914 disaster did not go sealing the next year. The *Stephano* was sent on war work and was sunk by a German submarine off the coast of Nantucket, Massachusetts, in October 1916. The *S.S. Newfoundland* reappeared in 1916, with her owner's and suppliers' names changed, herself transparently disguised as the *S.S. Samuel Blandford*. The *Blandford* was lost on the rocks in St. Mary's Bay in August of 1916.

For 20 years after the Newfoundland disaster Abram Kean continued to hunt seals. At the age of 79, after 67 seasons on the ice, he returned home with his millionth seal pelt, one record that never will be broken. For his efforts he was awarded the Order of the British Empire, in 1934.

The same storm that doomed the men of the *Newfoundland* claimed other victims as well. The *S.S. Southern Cross*, returning from the Gulf of St. Lawrence with its load of seals and carrying 173 men, was last sighted on the southern coast of Newfoundland off Cape Race. A few remnants from the ship washed up on the west coast of Ireland that summer.

By the end of the 1914 sealing season a total of 253 sealers and 234,000 seals had lost their lives.

With the onset of World War I later that year, the steel steamers were soon transferred to war service, leaving only the old wooden steamers to hunt seals. The 1915 season saw only 47,000 seals landed, the lowest catch since 1817. Between 1915 and 1919, the average annual catch dropped to 143,000 seals per year. However, since the price of seal oil rose during the war years to three or four times its normal value, sealing remained a profitable business.

After the war, oil prices dropped and there was little economic incentive to warrant the construction of new sealing vessels to refurbish the fleet. The 1920 catch dropped to a new low of 34,000. Nonetheless, the ship owners continued to look for ways to revitalize the seal fishery. As early as 1921, only 18 years after the Wright brothers' first flight in the *Flyer*, at Kitty Hawk, North Carolina, a bi-plane was used in an attempt to locate the seals before the sealing fleet departed St. John's. As with the introduction of the Dundee steamers decades earlier, this innovation was not an immediate success. It was not until 1 April that a flight of any distance was made, and no seals were sighted.

Processing seal oil.
Photo: Provincial
Archives of Newfound-
land & Labrador

FILLING DIGESTERS WITH FAT TO BE RENDERED INTO OIL. BOWRING BROS LTD ST JOHNS N.F.

126

Handling pelts on the
docks.
*Photo: Provincial
Archives of Newfound-
land & Labrador*

Levi Chafe describes the events of the following year, in his classic work, *Chafe's Sealing Book*:

> On March 16, 1922, the Martinsyde and Westland aero-
> planes, undertook a survey of the ice-fields ... Major Cotton
> [piloting the Martinsyde plane] reported large patches of
> seals, and negotiations were opened with the sealing
> owners for handing over the information obtained. Unfor-
> tunately about a week elapsed before a mutual agreement
> was reached, and by this time the information was no
> longer effective.

It took the owners no time to recognize the potentials offered by the use of aircraft to locate the depleted seal herds. The following year, 1923, Chafe reported that:

> the idea of operating a small aeroplane from one of the
> Sealing ships, is to be carried out. The "Antarctic Baby
> Avro" [a small bi-plane], which accompanied [Ernest]
> Shackleton on the *"Quest"* has been secured, and will
> shortly arrive in Newfoundland. [Shackleton's 1920-1921
> voyage on the *Quest* had ended abruptly with his death in
> South Georgia on 5 January 1921.]

Contemporary critics claimed that the introduction of aeroplanes to find the diminished seal herds would ensure their annihilation. Others, including Levi Chafe, suggested that the introduction of aeroplanes would minimize the 'gambling element', so that successful sealing voyages could be 'undertaken both by owners and men without any risk, or loss of time or money'.

Spotting the herd, 1933

Chafe also argued that 'most important in regard to the success of aerial reconnoitering is that it will eventually tend to the preservation of the seals'. He never did explain exactly how this would be achieved. Regardless, the use of aircraft for 'Spotting the Herd' became a fixture for finding the seals, a practice that continues today.

Between 1920 and 1929, an average of fewer than ten ships, carrying only 1,548 men, landed an average of 154,000 seals. And although between 1930 and 1939, the number of ships dropped to fewer than nine per year, and the number of men declined to 1,429, the average annual catch of the Newfoundland fleet rose slightly to 168,000 seals. The increased catches per man were interpreted by some to indicate that the seals were becoming more plentiful as a result of the decreased catches of the previous decades.

The year 1931 was the year of the last major sealing disaster. The wooden steamer, the *S.S. Viking*, carrying dynamite and gun powder to blast its way through the ice, blew up, killing 29 men, including the director of a Hollywood film crew who was on board to make a movie about the seal hunt.

The contribution of the harp seal to the economic history of Newfoundland was not forgotten in the 1932-1938 issue of postage stamps depicting the resources of the island.

Resources Issue, 1932-1938.

In 1934, Newfoundland, on the verge of bankruptcy, ceased to be a Dominion of the British Commonwealth of Nations, and reverted to the status of a British Crown Colony. It was subsequently governed by a Commission, consisting of a British Governor, three Commissioners, and three Newfoundlanders, all appointed by the British Government. Seals and the sealing fleet were once again honoured when the colony issued a new set of postage stamps commemorating the Coronation of King George VI in 1937.

As the decade of the Dirty '30s drew to a close, a new participant entered the Newfoundland seal hunt. Just as the Dundee sealers had come to Newfoundland in 1876 after depleting the Jan Mayen harp seals, Norwegian sealers, having participated in the reduction of the White Sea harp seals off the coast of Russia, came to Newfoundland in search of more seals.

The Norwegians made five trips to the Newfoundland ice before the Second World War. Beginning in 1937, they sent a single ship which landed almost 3,700 seals. Two ships came in 1938, landing an impressive 16,300 seals. Five ships came in 1939 and 1940, taking more than 30,000 seals in each year. Germany invaded Norway on 9 April 1940 and it seems that, instead of returning home, the five Norwegian ships landed their seals in Newfoundland and remained on this side of the Atlantic. By the following year, 1941, these five ships appear to have moved to Halifax, Nova Scotia where, under the name of Karlsen Shipping Company Ltd., they became the 'Canadian' large vessel sealing industry. From 1941 onward, the catches of the Karlsen ships were included in the Canadian, rather than Norwegian, catch statistics.

Coronation Issue, 1937.

Technically, Norway's sealing efforts off Newfoundland ended during the war. Two Norwegian ships participated in the 1941 hunt, but their identities and their catches seem to have gone unrecorded. After the war, ships from Norway would return to join their countrymen who had remained in Canada throughout the war. Together, they would dramatically change the face of the northwest Atlantic seal hunt once again.

As in the First War, the Newfoundland sealing fleet was again required for wartime service beginning in 1939. During the war years, annual catches by the Newfoundland sealers plummeted, reaching the lowest levels recorded since the 18th century. Newfoundland reported average landings of only 48,000 seals between 1940 and 1945. In 1943, for the first time in more than a century, no large ships prosecuted the seal fishery and no seals were reportedly taken. The last of the old wooden-walls, the *S.S. Eagle*, returned to the ice the following year and brought back fewer than 7,000 seals.

Landsmen on a floe.

Up until this time, Canada's participation in the Newfoundland seal hunt was largely confined to landsmen sealing along the North Shore of the St. Lawrence River and on the ice near the Magdalen Islands. Yet, prior to 1938, annual catch statistics from these Canadian landsmen hunts were not routinely compiled. Consequently, all the figures we have given previously for the numbers of seals landed annually do not include the catches of Canadian landsmen. Between 1940 and 1945, their catches accounted for almost 20,000 seals annually.

The 1945 hunt saw the introduction of yet another new type of sealing ship, the small, oil-powered motor vessel. Five such vessels from Newfoundland went sealing that year and brought back more than 11,000 seals.

With the reduced catches of seals and a lull in fishing activities throughout the war, the seals apparently prospered. But any recovery from centuries of exploitation was to be short-lived.

Post-war sealing

With the end of the war, and prices for seal oil high, there was an immediate resurgence in sealing activities off Newfoundland and in the Gulf of St. Lawrence. From this point on, detailed catch statistics for all segments of the hunt in these areas were kept.

In 1946, Newfoundland sent one wooden-wall and 11 small motor vessels to the hunt and landed almost 35,000 seals; Newfoundland landsmen took an additional 24,000; Norway returned to the hunt with one vessel and took home more than 7,500 seals; another 24,500 were taken by landsmen in the Gulf. Canada formally became more involved, for the first time sending several vessels –

Karlsen's transplanted Norwegian fleet – that took 17,000 seals in the Gulf. Landsmen in the Canadian Atlantic provinces accounted for another 1,000 seals.

The Norwegian ship *Novara* in the ice.
Photo: K. Ronald

Over the next four years, hunting effort escalated and between 1946 and 1949 the average annual catch from all quarters of the hunt increased to more than 200,000 seals. Coincidentally, it was in 1949 that, under the leadership of Joey Smallwood, Newfoundlanders voted by a narrow margin to join the Dominion of Canada as its tenth province. The Newfoundland seal hunt nominally became Canada's seal hunt.

After Confederation with Canada, Newfoundland's entrepreneurial interest in the hunt began to wane and Norwegian interests started to take control of the large vessel hunt. By 1969, only one Newfoundland-owned ship, Crosbie & Co.'s *Chesley A. Crosbie*, prosecuted the seal fishery. She was joined in 1970-71 by a second ship, the *Lady Johnson*. In 1972, however, not one Newfoundland vessel participated in the seal fishery. Since then, only one or two Newfoundland companies have sent large vessels back to the ice.

By the early 1970s, then, Canadian companies operated by Norwegian expatriates, Norwegian-owned subsidiaries operating in Canada and the Norwegian sealing industry had, in effect, taken over the 'Canadian' seal hunt. Between 1950 and 1970, they accounted for more than half of the annual catch of seals; they set the prices paid for pelts and controlled the bulk of the processing and marketing of seal products taken by all participants. Newfoundlanders manned many of their boats and Canadian landsmen depended on them to buy their pelts. As with most Canadian resource industries, Canada was merely the supplier of raw materials that other countries then processed and marketed to earn the bulk of the profits. But we are getting ahead of the story.

The escalation of sealing activities immediately after the war reached its zenith during the 1950s. Catches between 1950 and 1959 averaged about 312,000 seals per year, achieving a 20th century high of over 430,000 in 1951.

Throughout the history of sealing, oil and leather had been the objects of the hunt. It was only during the 1940s and 1950s that Norwegian innovations in the tanning of seal pelts provided a new incentive to kill seals – to produce tanned pelts for the fur industry. This innovation put additional pressures on the seals and particularly on the hooded seals which, although more difficult to hunt than harp seals, produced the prized blueback pelt, the most valuable of all hair seal pelts.

Another player entered the picture in the years after World War II. It was only then that scientists in the employ of the Government of Canada began the first attempts to assess the numbers of seals present and the levels of exploitation they could sustain. As early as 1952, Dr. H. Dean Fisher concluded: 'It seems obvious that with continuing kills in the order of that in 1951, the population would be unable to maintain itself and some restrictions would be needed....'

The scientists were particularly concerned about the large numbers of adult seals being killed. In 1960, Dr. David Sergeant warned, 'Under these conditions, and without imposition of effective controls, the stock of western Atlantic harp seals must be considered to be in grave danger of catastrophic decline in numbers within a very few years'. In a co-authored report, Sergeant and Fisher noted that their census figures indicated that the population had been halved between 1950 and 1960 and that 'the decline may have been even greater than this'.

In response to these warnings, closing dates were

imposed beginning in 1961 to limit the length of the sealing season in the Gulf of St. Lawrence and on the Front. Nonetheless, it would be several more years before any controls over the numbers of seals killed were implemented.

In 1961 and again in 1963, the USSR joined Canada and Norway in the seal hunt off Newfoundland, accounting for 11,400 and 17,500 seals in the two years, respectively. But the Russians did not pursue this experiment and returned to their traditional sealing grounds in the northeast Atlantic, operating primarily from state farms along the coast of the White Sea.

During the 1960s, catches in the northwest Atlantic declined somewhat, averaging 284,000 seals per year between 1960 and 1969. The decline might have been greater had the industry not extended its use of aircraft in sealing. Beginning in 1962, aeroplanes and helicopters were employed not only to locate the seals, but also to ferry men from the Magdalen Islands and Prince Edward Island to the ice floes in the Gulf of St. Lawrence to hunt seals, and to transport the seal pelts to shore. Helicopters were also used to assist the large vessels operating in the Gulf.

It would take more than the warnings of scientists to change the nature of the seal hunt.

Years of controversy, 1964-

Until 1964, the seal hunt came and went each year without much fanfare. Occasional accounts of the hunt had appeared, such as a 1929 *National Geographic* article written by Captain Bob Bartlett. Bartlett, from a line of famous sealers, was also well known for his involvement in Arctic exploration with Stefansson and Peary. Incidentally, he also represents another link between Newfoundland and British polar exploration, having bid farewell to Robert Scott as the *Terra Nova* departed from the docks of London on 1 June 1910 for its ill-fated voyage to Antarctica.

Several books were also written, most notably, George Allen England's *Vikings of the Ice*, an eye-witness account of the 1922 hunt aboard the *Terra Nova* under

Captain Abram Kean, and Major William Howe Greene's 1933 classic, *The Wooden Walls Among the Ice Floes, Telling the Romance of the Newfoundland Seal Fishery*. But these, and the occasional article published during the 1950s, seem to have made little impression on the world at large.

It was during the 1950s that observers from various humane societies first went to the hunt and began to express their concern about the cruelty involved in killing seals. By the early 1960s, tales of 'the mass destruction of seals' began to appear in Canadian newspapers. The public was slowly becoming aware of the the seal hunt.

Then, on 16 March 1964, television brought the seal hunt, for the first time, into the living rooms of Canada and the world. The photogenic whitecoats and the dark blood on white ice made an everlasting impression. Such is the power of television.

The film in question was made by Artek Films Ltd., a small Canadian company under contract to *Radio Canada*, the French language television network of the Canadian Broadcasting Corporation. The debate continues today on the legitimacy of the footage, on whether it accurately portrayed the Canadian seal hunt, or whether some scenes were actually staged using a few young and inexperienced sealers, possibly under the influence of alcohol.

In reality, such questions are entirely academic. The film gave immediate publicity and credence to the claims of cruelty that had begun to circulate in recent years. In both North America and Europe, the anti-sealing movement was born.

The man who emerged as the leader of the anti-sealing movement, a position he can still rightfully claim today, was Brian Davies. Davies initially became involved as a part-time officer with the New Brunswick Society for the Prevention of Cruelty to Animals (SPCA). After an aborted trip to the ice in 1965, he first observed the hunt in 1966. Within three years he established the International Fund for Animal Welfare (IFAW). From its inception, the IFAW was, as it remains today, dedicated to ending the commercial exploitation of seals.

With pressure mounting from scientists and animal welfare groups, the Canadian Government began to respond. In 1965, it implemented the *Seal Protection Regu-*

lations. These regulations introduced controls on the methods of killing seals and required, for the first time, the licensing of sealing vessels, aircraft and sealers. Adult female harp seals were protected on whelping patches (they could still be killed later in the season on the moulting patches), Norway was excluded from sealing in the Gulf of St. Lawrence and Canadian sealers operating in this region were, for the first time, limited to killing 50,000 seals.

It was also in 1965 that 'management' of seals in international waters beyond Canada's 12 mile limit was put under the auspices of the International Commission for the Northwest Atlantic Fisheries (ICNAF), with the active sealing nations – Canada, Norway and Denmark (on behalf of Greenland) – as voting members.

By 1966, Dr. Wilfred Templeman, a Canadian government scientist who 20 years later would be a member of the Royal Commission on Seals and Sealing, declared that 'the herd is being gradually destroyed and sealing practices will have to be changed to kill fewer young and especially fewer female adults'.

That same year, Dr. Douglas Pimlott, a biology professor at the University of Toronto, went to the ice as a representative for the Canadian Audubon Society. In an article published the following year, Pimlot concluded:

Club or Bat.

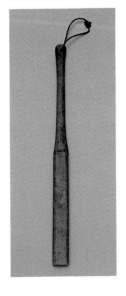

The industry is greedy, it is overcapitalized and it holds a very short-term view of the resources. If it prevails in its demand for higher annual quotas than the seal population can sustain, the harp seals of the Front herd are likely to be exterminated within this century.

A spokesman for the sealing industry, reflecting on this period in a Brief submitted to the Royal Commission on Seals and Sealing in Canada in the mid-1980s, expressed it this way:

... we could see that the catching effort was too great and that probably quotas would be required.

Until 1966, there were few limitations on the methods of killing seals. Whitecoats and bluebacks were normally dispatched with a blow to the head using a wooden club

Hakapik heads.

(similar in size and appearance to a baseball bat), a gaff (a long, wooden-handled instrument with a sharp metal point and hook bound to the business end) or a Norwegian **hakapik** (an iron head with a curved spike on one side and a short, blunt projection on the other, mounted on a wooden handle up to 1.5 meters (5 feet) in length). Beaters and older seals were usually shot using a variety of guns and rifles although some adult harp and hooded seals were also killed by clubbing.

In 1967, the *Seal Protection Regulations* banned the use of the gaff as a killing instrument and provided specifications for the clubs, rifles and shotguns that could be used to kill seals. Although these specifications have evolved slightly over the succeeding years, the club and *hakapik* are still used to kill young seals and guns are used to dispatch older animals.

Clubbing and sculping a whitecoat.
Photo: K. Ronald

Sealing – using a *hakapik*.

By 1970, the use of aircraft to hunt seals was prohibited and, in 1971, the ICNAF introduced quota management with a view to limiting catches of harp seals in the northwest Atlantic. Although there is now general agreement that the harp seal population declined by at least 50 per cent between 1950 and 1970, and perhaps by as much as 66 per cent, this significant step was not only motivated by the scientific evidence. The decision to limit the catch of harp seals was also influenced by the rapidly growing and increasingly vocal anti-sealing movement. The introduction of quota management for the less accessible and less well known hooded seals would have to wait.

The initial quota for the entire northwest Atlantic seal hunt on the Front and in the Gulf of St. Lawrence was 245,000 harp seals. This quota provided the two large

Theta.
Photo: K. Ronald

vessel sealing fleets operating out of Canada and Norway with 100,000 animals each; the remaining 45,000 was an unregulated allotment for Canadian landsmen from Newfoundland, the North Shore of the St. Lawrence River and the Magdalen Islands. In other words, the imposition of quotas did not totally limit the number of harp seals that could be killed. If the large vessels reached their quota and the landsmen had a good year and exceeded their allotment, the 'quota' would be surpassed. As it turned out, the sealers fell short of their quota in 1971, landing about 231,000 seals (a summary of quota management and catches from 1971 to 1987 is provided in the Table on page 137).

Sealers with their catch.
Photo: K. Ronald

The implementation of the *Seal Protection Regulations*, and the introduction of quotas notwithstanding, the Canadian Government was still under intense public pressure to end the seal hunt. So in 1971, the Minister of the Environment, The Hon. Jack Davis, announced the formation of a Special Advisory Committee on Seals and Sealing (COSS) 'to review all aspects of seals and sealing'. In its 'Interim Report', released on 18 January 1972, COSS recommended that the Canadian and Norwegian Atlantic seal hunt be phased out by 1974 and that this should be followed by a minimum six-year moratorium on hunting.

This recommendation was never implemented. Instead, the quotas introduced a year earlier were drastically reduced to 150,000 seals for the 1972 season. Whether

Quotas and catch statistics for harp seals on the 'Front' off Newfoundland and in the Gulf of St. Lawrence, 1971-1987

Year	Quota[1]	Catch[2]
1971	245,000	230,966
1972	150,000	129,883
1973	150,000	123,832
1974	150,000	147,635
1975	150,000	174,363
1976	127,000	165,002
1977	160,000	155,143
1978	170,000	161,723
1979	170,000	160,541
1980	170,000	171,929
1981	168,200	200,162
1982	175,000	166,739
1983	175,000	57,889
1984	175,000	30,900
1985	175,000	18,225
1986	175,000	24,532[3]
1987	175,000	49,000[3]

[1] 'Quota' refers only to the hunt by Canada and Norway off Newfoundland and in the Gulf of St. Lawrence. For the years 1971-1976, part of this quota was an unregulated allotment for landsmen that was intended to represent the expected catch.

[2] 'Catch' includes only those harp seals killed on the Front and in the Gulf of St. Lawrence. It does not include harp seals killed off west Greenland or in the eastern Canadian Arctic during the summer months. (From figures obtained from Sealing Statistics compiled by ICNAF and subsequently, by NAFO, and by the Canadian Department of Fisheries and Oceans.)

[3] preliminary figures

this had anything to do with the COSS report or the general belief among scientists that the seals simply could not sustain the 1971 quota (remember the sealers were unable to reach the quota in 1971) is not entirely clear.

From 1972 to 1975, the anti-sealing movement continued its protests and the quota remained unchanged. For the first three years, the sealers' catches again fell short of

138

1974.

the quota, but in 1975 it was exceeded by 24,000 animals. This was the result of a particularly successful landsmen hunt which, you will remember, was not regulated at the time.

It was during this time that the seals drew the attention of a new enterprise – tourism. As early as 1969, Brian Davies had suggested that tourism provided an alternative to the seal hunt in the Gulf of St. Lawrence. To demonstrate his point, he organized a small symbolic tour to the ice floes in March of 1970.

In 1974, the first 'commercial' tour was attempted. A small group of tourists arrived at the tiny airport in the Magdalen Islands only to be met by one of the first pro-sealing, protest demonstrations. The tourists were trapped at the airport for about two hours before being allowed to proceed to their hotel in Grindstone (Cap-aux-Meules). But the initial hostility quickly dissipated and within days several landsmen sealers were acting as tour guides on the ice.

'Prosealing' protest demonstration greets the first tourists to arrive at the airport in the Magdalen Islands in March 1974. Note that *phoque* is French for 'seal'.

For several years thereafter, small numbers of tourists arrived annually in the 'Maggies'. Many of these were members of conservation groups and animal welfare organizations who wanted to see the seals for themselves. But the venture did not take off and, for a variety of reasons, commercial tours to the ice lapsed by 1981.

It was also in 1974 that a quota was introduced to limit the number of hooded seals killed. Throughout the entire history of the seal hunt, hooded seals had always been taken as a by-catch of the harp seal fishery. Catches of hooded seals, however, tended to vary more from year to year than those of harp seals. This was probably because hooded seals, being relatively scarce, were more difficult to find and, possibly, because the location of their whelping patches seems to change rather dramatically with minor changes in climate.

The hooded seal hunt differed from the harp seal hunt in one important way. Whereas the harp seal hunt was primarily directed at pups, the hunt for hooded seals usually took a large number of adults, particularly breeding females that remain on the ice with their pups.

The practice of killing both pups and their mothers is similar to withdrawing both interest and capital from a bank account. Consistently, one Canadian government scientist suggested that if the Newfoundland hooded seals had belonged to an isolated population, they would long ago have been exterminated by the fishery. This line of reasoning requires that the hooded seals breeding in the Davis Strait served as a reservoir that replenished the Newfoundland herd throughout the 20th century.

Regardless, the 1974 quota of 15,000 hooded seals did little to protect the breeding population from further depletion. Such steps were taken between 1977 and 1979 when the proportion of adult females was progressively reduced from ten, to seven and a half, to five per cent of the total allowable catch. (For a summary of quotas and catches for hooded seals, see the Table on p. 140).

During the summer and fall of 1975, Canadian scientists, conducting their annual assessment of the harp seals in the northwest Atlantic, found evidence that the population was not in nearly as good shape as they had previously believed, despite the introduction of quotas several years before. Figures were checked and rechecked, additional analyses were conducted, but the answer remained the same – the population was in trouble. So serious was the situation, it seemed at the time, that one prominent senior Canadian government scientist was moved to suggest that:

> Any serious attempt to salvage the harp seal herd as a commercially important resource requires the immediate

Quotas and catch statistics for hooded seals on the 'Front' off Newfoundland, 1974-1987

Year	Quota	Catch[1]
1974	15,000	9,995
1975	15,000	15,611
1976	15,000	12,385
1977	15,000	12,093
1978	15,000	10,223
1979	15,000	15,125
1980	15,000	13,053
1981	15,000	13,686
1982	15,000	10,393
1983	12,000	128
1984	2,340	444
1985	2,340	784
1986	2,340	33[2]
1987	2,340	2,008[2]

[1] includes small numbers of hooded seals killed in the Gulf of St. Lawrence but not those animals killed off west Greenland. (From figures obtained from Sealing Statistics compiled by ICNAF and subsequently, by NAFO, and by the Canadian Department of Fisheries and Oceans.)

[2] preliminary figures.

cessation of all commercial sealing for at least 10 years, leaving only the arctic subsistence catch at no more than the present level. Anything less than this is fiddling while Rome burns; in fact, it is fiddling after 80% of the city has already been consumed.

Norwegian scientists argued that the Canadian assessments were overly pessimistic or just plain wrong. Nonetheless, the harp seal quota was reduced to 127,000 for 1976, based on the least pessimistic of the Canadian assessments available at the time.

With the renewed suggestions that the harp seal herd was depleted and possibly could not sustain the levels of hunting dictated by ICNAF and the Government of Canada, protests against the seal hunt began to escalate again in 1976. More groups became involved in the anti-sealing movement and most significantly, perhaps, *Green-*

peace entered the fray. (The fact that *Greenpeace* first became involved in the sealing controversy in 1976 seems to be lost on most contemporary writers, at least in Canada, who seem to synonymize *Greenpeace* with the anti-sealing movement, and credit (or blame) this organization for just about everything that has happened to the seal hunt and the sealing industry during the past two decades. Like *Xerox, Greenpeace* is in danger of becoming a generic name.)

The original Greenpeace flag ship, the *Rainbow Warrior,* in the Gulf in March 1984.
Photo: R. Frank

There is no doubt that the high profile presence of *Greenpeace*, their acts of civil disobedience and their ability to generate media coverage and publicity, together with the activities of the other groups involved, kept the seal hunt in the public eye more than ever before. At this time, the major concerns of the animal welfare community and

The *Sea Shepherd* protest ship with Captain Paul Watson challenges sealers in 1979.
Photo: N. Lightfoot

1945.

the environmental movement were two-fold: concern about the cruelty to animals associated with the seal hunt and concern that the seal populations might well be endangered by further over-exploitation.

As it turned out, the reduction in the quota for 1976, motivated by scientific concerns, had little effect on the catch that year. As with the previous year, the unregulated landsmen hunt exceeded the expected catch (their allotment), this time by almost 40,000 seals. As the large vessels essentially met their quota, the total catch surpassed the quota by a similar amount; it exceeded the quota of the previous year, that only months before had been judged too high. Such results gave substance to the anti-sealing movement's claims that the hunt was not carefully regulated and that the seals were therefore threatened.

After the 1976 hunt, the scientists went back to the drawing board. They redid their analyses of the previous year and found that things were perhaps not as bad as they had seemed only 12 months before. Such was the uncertainty in the available data and analyses. As a result, the quota was raised to 160,000 for 1977, with an additional allotment of 10,000 for the summer hunts in the eastern Canadian Arctic and west Greenland. This was the first real acknowledgement that, throughout the entire history of the Newfoundland seal hunt, harp seals were also hunted in northern waters during the summer. For example, average annual catches of harp seals in west Greenland during the 1940s add an additional 22,000 animals to the statistics given earlier. Catches declined to about 7,000 animals during the 1970s, consistent with other evidence that the population had indeed declined substantially after the war. Innuit in the eastern Canadian Arctic also routinely take several hundred to a few thousand harp seals each year, although accurate statistics from these hunts are only rarely available.

On 1 January 1977, Canada followed the example of many maritime nations and declared a 200-mile economic zone along its extensive coastline. This gave Canada exclusive control over the traditional sealing grounds off Newfoundland and in the Gulf of St. Lawrence. Since harp and hooded seals also spend time within Greenland's (i.e. Denmark's) 200-mile limit, it also meant that principal

The Innuit seal hunt in the eastern Canadian Arctic.
Photo: N. Lightfoot

responsibility for managing the seal herds in the northwest Atlantic now fell to Canada and Denmark, representing Greenland. Norway's continued involvement was maintained through bi-lateral agreement with Canada. To reflect the restructuring of the northwest Atlantic fishery and to provide a mechanism for 'multilateral co-operation' in the new era of extended national fisheries jurisdiction, the International Commission for the Northwest Atlantic Fisheries (ICNAF) was transformed into the Northwest Atlantic Fisheries Organization (NAFO).

With increased control over the east coast seal hunt, Canada showed no signs of giving in to the protests of the anti-sealing movement. Early in 1978, the Government of Newfoundland and Labrador, with the support of the Federal Government, organized a publicity campaign to justify the continuation of the annual seal hunt. Led by the Premier of Newfoundland and Labrador, The Hon. Frank D. Moores, a delegation that included representatives of the Federal Department of Fisheries, some members of the Committee on Seals and Sealing, and a 'marine biologist', travelled to major centres in the United States and Europe to give 'Canada's side of the sealing story'. In addition, Canadian journalists were sent by the Govenment to far-off places to 'educate' the world press about the 'facts' of the Canadian seal hunt.

Although one can appreciate the desire of the proponents of sealing to tell their side of the story, the participation of the Committee on Seals and Sealing and Canadian journalists in this exercise raised questions about their ability to function as independent arbiters and objective reporters of the seal-hunt controversy. Equally telling was the fact that the only 'scientist' involved in this exercise was a medical doctor, with no particular expertise on seals. Not once were any of the Canadian government scientists who were actively involved in the assessment process given the opportunity to explain their 'facts'.

Consistent with the Canadian Government's support of the seal hunt, the total allowable catch for 1978 was increased an additional 10,000 over that of the previous year to 170,000. It remained at this level for the 1979 and 1980 sealing seasons. Despite the continued protests of the anti-sealing movement, harp seal quotas and catches were on the rise again (see Table, p. 137).

In retrospect, the pro-sealing publicity campaign served to escalate the public controversy surrounding the seal hunt. Every appearance of pro-sealing spokesmen on television was accompanied by vivid footage of the seal hunt. The pictures spoke for themselves. Anti-sealers also confronted the pro-sealers at their press conferences and this was dutifully reported in the press and shown on television. Nonetheless, in 1981 and 1982, the quotas for harp seals rose again. In 1981, the catch exceeded 200,000 animals for the first time in a decade; it also exceeded the

The *Technoventure* sealing in the Gulf during the 1980s. *Photo: R. Frank*

The *Brandel* sealing in the Gulf.
Photo: N. Lightfoot

total allowable catch by almost 20,000 animals, once again raising questions about the Canadian Government's ability, or willingness, to carefully regulate the seal hunt.

Throughout the late 1970s and early 1980s, the anti-sealing movement continued its protests in the Gulf of St. Lawrence and on the Front in early March. But they were losing ground. As a result, the IFAW and several other groups shifted their attention to Europe. From their perspective, this made sense on at least two fronts. Since the showing of the 1964 Artek film, many Europeans had opposed the seal hunt and thousands had joined anti-sealing groups. Most importantly, Europe was the major market for seal products.

In one confrontation during March 1984, the IFAW chopper was damaged by proponents of the seal hunt at the airport in the Magdalen Islands.

As a result of the stepped-up, anti-sealing campaign, increasing numbers of Europeans began to speak out against the seal hunt. In 1980, Euro-MP Mr. Stanley Johnson, from the United Kingdom, proposed a motion in the European Parliament calling on the European Commission to ban the importation into the European Economic Community (EEC) of products derived from harp and hooded seal pups (specifically from whitecoats and bluebacks). The motion was referred to the Committee on the Environment, Public Health and Consumer Protection chaired by Mrs. J. Maij-Weggen of the Netherlands.

By late 1981, the Committee had produced a Report that included a proposed resolution calling for a ban on trade in products derived from young harp and hooded seals. On 11 March 1982, after receiving petitions signed by several million of their constituents, the European Parliament adopted the resolution by a vote of 160 to 10.

In itself, the European Parliament cannot implement legislation but can only make recommendations to the European Commission, which may or may not pass these on to the ultimate decision-making body – the European Council of Ministers. Nonetheless, the discussions in Europe and the vote in the European parliament, occurring as they did in the middle of the 1982 seal hunt, did nothing to improve the already declining markets for seal products and, without the promise of good prices for their efforts, the sealers' catch of harp seals dropped in 1982 to less than 167,000.

What happened next is well known. After months of discussion and indecision, the European Economic Community instituted a temporary, two-year ban on the importation of products from harp and hooded seal pups on 1 October 1983. The Canadian Government was disappointed that it had been unable to ward off the European ban and looked for a way to ensure that it would not be extended beyond its initial deadline of 30 September 1985.

During the summer of 1984, the Canadian Government appointed a Royal Commission on Seals and the Sealing Industry to examine all aspects of seals and sealing in Canada. The Commission was to produce its final report on 30 September 1985, the very last day before the European ban would have to be renewed or allowed to lapse

Perhaps the Canadian Government was hoping that the EEC would reserve future decisions until it had considered the Royal Commission's Report. When it became clear that the Royal Commission would not be able to meet its deadline, Canada asked the EEC to put off any decision on renewing the ban until the Report was ready – then said to be in late December 1985.

The Europeans did not wait. On 27 September 1985, before the original EEC Directive had lapsed, and before the original deadline for the Royal Commission Report, the temporary ban was extended for an additional four years, to 1 October 1989.

The effect of the European ban on the seal hunt was immediate and can easily be seen by examining the subsequent catches of harp and hooded seals (see Tables, pp. 137 and 140). Norwegian vessels stopped going to the hunt as did the Canadian large vessels from Nova Scotia and Newfoundland. Some landsmen in Newfoundland and in the Magdalen Islands continued to seal but harp seal catches between 1983 and 1987 dropped to an average of about 36,000 animals per year.

The Royal Commission Report did not appear in December 1985 and rumoured dates for its appearance came and went through most of 1986. Its major conclusions and recommendations were finally made public during the summer of 1986, not in the form of its Report, but in the form of a leak to CBC television. The Report finally appeared on 17 December 1986 when the Minister of Fisheries and Oceans, The Hon. Thomas Siddon, rose in the House of Commons and simply announced, 'under the provisions of Standing Order 67(2), I wish to table in both official languages the report of the Royal Commission on Seals and Sealing in Canada'. By this time, the Royal Commission was old news and its publication generated little interest, not only in The House of Commons, but in the media and elsewhere.

The Report itself consisted of three volumes, over 1,360 pages of text. These volumes should be read with care. The short summary, Volume 1, provides an overly simplistic and biased view of the subject. Although Volumes 2 and 3 provide more extensive and more balanced coverage of the complex issues involved, they do not always present the facts accurately. And some of the Royal Commission's major conclusions and recommendations are based on erroneous calculations.

Nonetheless, the Royal Commission made a number of noteworthy recommendations. It concluded that the 'commercial hunting' of the pups of harp seals (whitecoats) and hooded seals (bluebacks) is widely unacceptable to the public and should not be permitted. It did not, however, rule out the possibility of 'non-commercial hunting' of such pups or the possibility that seal pups might be killed in the future as a measure of population control. 'In view of the suffering involved,' it also recommended that the Government phase out the netting of seals as rapidly as possible. Importantly for the sealers, the Commission advocated generous compensation for lost income and for other losses associated with the demise of markets for seal products. It remains to be seen which, if any, of the Commission's recommendations will be implemented, in whole or in part, by the Government of Canada.

In the interim, the seal hunt continues. In 1987, two large vessels from Canada returned to the ice for the first time in five years. They landed a small catch, fewer than 4,000 seals. Landsmen accounted for another 45,000 animals.

In the Gulf of St. Lawrence, there have been renewed attempts to take tourists to the ice to see the seals, a development supported by the Committee on Seals and Sealing and by the Royal Commission. Tourists returned to the ice in 1986 and 1987, in larger numbers than ever before.

Tourists in the Gulf.

Tours now operate from Charlottetown, Prince Edward Island, and to a lesser extent, from the Magdalen Islands.

As the story of *Harps & Hoods* continues to unfold it is difficult to predict what will happen next. We will briefly examine some of the prospects for seals and sealing in the final chapter.

6. Future Prospects

The days are getting warmer. The snow in town is melting and the ice in the Gulf of St. Lawrence is breaking up and quickly moving southeastward through the Cabot Strait, past Cape Breton and beyond. Each day we have to fly further to find seals and, even then, there are fewer seals to be found. The breeding rituals of the harp and hooded seals are almost over and our field work in the Gulf is drawing to a close for another year.

In search of seals.

The seals will once again wend their way toward summer feeding grounds in the north, only to return southward in the fall. Throughout the year, they will be hunted by coastal inhabitants along the entire length of their migration route, from the Gulf of St. Lawrence to the high Arctic and back, as they have been for centuries. The annual cycle will continue. So will the debate about the pros and cons of the annual seal hunt.

◀ Dawn in the Gulf.
Photo: N. Lightfoot

Sealers will continue their efforts to revitalize the seal hunt. They will argue that their methods of killing seals are humane, that the seal hunt is an important part of their tradition and culture and that it provides an important source of income for coastal communities in eastern Canada. They will be vigorously opposed by the anti-sealing movement. Those against sealing will continue to claim that the methods used to kill seals are cruel and inhumane; they will argue that the products of the hunt are nonessential, even trivial; they will remember past failures to manage the seal hunt and will maintain that renewed commercial sealing will once again threaten the long-term survival of the seal herds.

The debate over most of these issues has become largely academic. Many sealers (and fishermen) now argue that even if there were no commercial seal hunt it would still be necessary to cull seal populations in order to limit their impact on commercial fisheries. On the other side, most anti-sealing groups have adopted the stance that they are simply opposed to commercial sealing and they do not accept the arguments that a seal hunt or a cull is necessary to limit the number of seals.

Sunset.
Photo: N. Lightfoot

The Gulf in March.

Harp seal pup.
Photo: N. Lightfoot

Hooded seal.
Photo: N. Lightfood

Late in the season ...
males cruising.

Consequently, future debates about seals and sealing in eastern Canada will revolve increasingly around questions about the possible interactions between seals and fisheries. This is a complex subject and one that is often misunderstood.

There is a wide-spread belief in the world today that marine mammals are having adverse effects on fisheries. Long before the European ban on seal products, fishermen and sealers (most of whom are themselves fishermen) in eastern Canada were complaining that there were too many seals, particularly too many harp seals. They claimed that the numbers of seals were increasing and that, because of the seals' 'voracious' appetites, higher quotas were required to protect important fisheries. With fewer seals being killed by hunters since the imposition of the European ban in 1983, many fishermen and sealers now believe that the seals are increasing at even faster rates. This is one of the reasons that they are calling for a revitalization of the sealing industry or, failing that, for the implementation of a government-controlled cull.

Nowhere have the arguments of the fishermen and sealers been more succinctly stated than in Canada's usually staid and self-proclaimed 'National Newspaper', *The Globe and Mail*. An editorial that appeared on 13 November 1985 began:

> The International Fund for Animal Welfare must be working overtime to rationalize this one. The seals they worked so hard to save from being killed in the annual Canadian hunt have stripped off their cute white disguises and emerged as messy, slobbering creatures whose chief contribution to the balance of nature is to fight fishermen for the diminishing supply of shrimp, cod, crab and capelin and to infect the remaining fish with worms.... The more seals there are, the worse the problem gets...

The editorial concluded with this suggestion:

> Perhaps it's time for a new publicity campaign: a photograph of sickly, helpless cod cowering in terror as tens of thousands of enormous seals converge on the coastal waters, devouring every fish they can catch and spreading disease and pestilence in their wake. Can nothing be done to rid us of this menace?

The arguments favouring renewed sealing or a controlled cull *seem* pretty straightforward. Everyone knows that seals eat fish. If they carry parasites and disease as well, then common sense dictates that these problems will only get worse if the numbers of seals increase. The only logical solution, it would appear, is to reduce the numbers of seals. Appearances are, however, often misleading.

In recent years, scientists have addressed many of the issues raised about the perceived interactions between harp (and hooded) seals and commercial fisheries. Their findings shed a different light on the presumed need for controlling seal populations.

Claims that the seal populations in the northwest Atlantic are increasing are a case in point. Today there may be somewhere between one and two million harp seals, perhaps even more; the number of pups born each year may be fewer than 300,000 or more than 500,000. It is not unreasonable to expect some increase in population size as a result of the smaller hunts of recent years, other things being equal – especially the availability of food. But whether the harp seal population is actually increasing in numbers is quite another question. At least three major scientific assessments have been undertaken in the last five years. In each instance, the scientists were not able to say with certainty that the population was increasing; moreover, they were unable to rule out the possibility that the population might even be declining.

Even less is known about hooded seals. Because scientists cannot accurately delineate hooded seal populations, it is virtually impossible to assess how many of these animals occur off Newfoundland and in the Gulf of St. Lawrence, let alone to determine trends in their abundance. Such uncertainties about the size of seal populations and trends in abundance are not surprising, considering the numbers of animals involved and their wide distribution.

As with the claims about the rapidly escalating numbers of seals, there is also reason to believe, to quote the *New York Times* from March 1984, that 'seals do not possess the vacuum cleaner appetites formerly assumed.' As we noted in Chapter 4, the food requirements of marine mammals such as seals are, for their size, similar to those of other mammals. It now seems that the amount of commercial fish consumed by northwest Atlantic harp seals has been overestimated in the past by as much as five to tenfold. Any potential impact that harp seals might have on fisheries must, therefore, be far less than is frequently claimed.

With reference to the specific examples raised in *The Globe and Mail* editorial cited above, there is no evidence that the seals are 'fight[ing] fishermen for the diminishing supply of shrimp, cod, crab and capelin.' If anything, capelin stocks are currently increasing; there is no evidence that 'shrimp' are in diminished supply; cod are not a particularly important prey species for harp seals; and 'crab' are rarely, if ever, eaten by these animals. In fact, scientists have been unable to find any examples of direct competition between harp (or hooded) seals and commercial fisheries in the northwest Atlantic. Recognizing the efficiency of modern fishing fleets, they have expressed some concern, however, that commercial fisheries could potentially threaten seal populations by reducing the availability of their prey.

Scientists have also noted that harp and hooded seals are relatively unimportant hosts of the codworm, the parasite that ends up in the flesh of cod and other commercially important fish. Viewed in this light, most of the problems outlined above have little, if anything, to do with the numbers of harp and hooded seals in the northwest Atlantic.

We must now consider whether a rejuvenated seal hunt or a controlled cull would improve the lot of fishermen. Given that in the late 1970s, quotas for harp seals were in excess of 180,000 animals and fishermen were already calling for increased quotas to protect fisheries, we must also ask how many animals would have to be killed in order to satisfy fishermen and sealers?

Scientists have admitted that they do not know precisely what effects decreasing (or increasing) the size of harp and hooded seal populations in the northwest Atlantic would have on commercial fisheries. Nonetheless, the claim that what the seals eat, fishermen do not catch, may lead to the conclusion that the fewer the seals, the larger the catches of fish. Such a conclusion is, however, both naive and incorrect.

If harp and hooded seals were reduced in numbers, other predators in the northwest Atlantic, including other seals, whales, seabirds and fish, might well fill the void and eat any 'surplus' prey, long before a fishery was able to reap the expected benefits. Furthermore, much of the prey eaten by these seals is of no commercial value or is consumed by seals in northern regions, far beyond the limits of traditional commercial fisheries. Therefore, the fishery cannot possibly catch all of the fish that would have been eaten by the culled seals. Thus, there might well be no detectable increase in the fishermen's catches. In cases where seals feed on the predator of a commercially important fish, one can envision the situation where culling seals might even result in a decline in that fishery. In conclusion, there is little reason to believe that culling harp and hooded seals will do anything to improve the lot of fishermen in eastern Canada.

If seal hunting were not rejuvenated and if no culling program were implemented, scientists would not expect seal populations to increase without limit. Harp seals, for example, are thought to be food-limited and sooner or later their numbers would be controlled naturally, largely by the availability of food. Food availability influences the growth rates of young animals, the age at which they reach sexual maturity and, for females, the age at which they first begin to reproduce. Thus, as the population increases towards its **carrying capacity**, the rate of reproduction will decline. Rates of natural mortality may also increase. Eventually, births will approximately balance deaths and the population will stabilize, even in the absence of human intervention.

At just what size a particular population will stabilize is impossible to predict. Given the changes in the northwest Atlantic ecosystem in the last three decades, many of them due to over-fishing by humans, it is quite possible that harp seals, for example, would not reach their former levels of abundance. When seals were more abundant than they are today, for example during the post-war years, fish stocks were also larger and no one was seriously suggesting that the seals were limiting the availability of fish.

In the final analysis, the future of the commercial seal hunt in eastern Canada will hinge not on scientific arguments about population control but on the availability of markets for seal products. The seal hunt will be rejuvenated only if there is an economic incentive for its rejuvenation. That is the way it was in the beginning and that is the way it will always be. Consequently, unless new markets can be developed, the future of the seal hunt will depend almost entirely on whether the European Economic Community renews its temporary import ban after reviewing the situation in the months and years leading up to October 1989.

Tourists on the ice.
LEFT photo: S. Innes
RIGHT photo: R. Vogel
– IFAW

Meanwhile, harp and hooded seals will return to the ice off Newfoundland and in the Gulf of St. Lawrence next spring. The tourist industry is optimistic that increasing numbers of people will take the opportunity to visit the seals on the ice. With luck, we too will return to continue our research on these fascinating animals. Maybe we will see you there.

Tourists?

Selected readings

A number of the titles given below are from papers published in the 'scientific literature'. These should be available in almost any university library, as will the majority of book titles listed. Some of the books will also be found in many public libraries.

1. Introduction

King, J.E. 1983. *Seals of the world*. Second edition. British Museum (Natural History) and Oxford University Press, Oxford, UK.

Reeves, R.R. and J.K. Ling. 1981. Hooded seal – *Cystophora cristata*. pp. 171-194. *In* S.H. Ridgway and R.J. Harrison (eds.). *Handbook of marine mammals. Volume 2. Seals*. Academic Press, London, UK.

Ronald, K. and P.J. Healey. 1981. Harp seal – *Phoca groenlandica*. pp. 55-87. *In* S.H. Ridgway and R.J. Harrison (eds.). *Handbook of marine mammals. Volume 2. Seals*. Academic Press, London, UK.

2. Distribution and Migration

Kovacs, K.M. and D.M. Lavigne. 1986. *Cystophora cristata*. Mammalian Species, 258:1-9.

Sergeant, D.E. 1965. Migrations of harp seals *Pagophilus groenlandicus* (Erxleben) in the northwest Atlantic. Journal of the Fisheries Research Board of Canada, 23:433-464.

Sergeant, D.E. 1974. A rediscovered whelping population of hooded seals *Cystophora cristata* Erxleben and their possible relations to other populations. Polarforschung, 44:1-7.

3. Life Cycles

Bowen, W.D., O.T. Oftedal and D.J. Boness. 1985. Birth to weaning in four days: Remarkable growth in the hooded seal, *Cystophora cristata*. Canadian Journal of Zoology, 63:2841-2846.

Bowen, W.D., D.J. Boness and O.T. Oftedal. 1987. Mass transfer from mother to pup and subsequent mass loss by the weaned pup in the hooded seal, *Cystophora cristata*. Canadian Journal of Zoology, 65:1-8.

Kovacs, K.M. 1987. Maternal behaviour and early behavioural ontogeny of harp seals, *Phoca groenlandica*. Animal Behaviour, 35:844-855.

Kovacs, K.M. and D.M. Lavigne. 1985. Neonatal growth and organ allometry of Northwest Atlantic harp seals (*Phoca groenlandica*). Canadian Journal of Zoology, 63:2793-2799.

Kovacs, K.M., D.M. Lavigne and R.E.A. Stewart. 1985. Early postnatal mortality in Northwest Atlantic harp seals, *Phoca groenlandica*. Journal of Mammalogy, 66:556-558.

Lavigne, D.M., S. Innes, R.E.A. Stewart and G.A.J. Worthy. 1985. An annual energy budget for North-west Atlantic harp seals. pp. 319-336. *In* J.R. Beddington, R.J.H. Beverton and D.M. Lavigne (eds.). *Marine mammals and fisheries.* George Allen & Unwin, London.

Stewart, R.E.A., S. Innes and N. Lightfoot. 1981. Parturition in harp seals. Journal of Mammalogy, 62:845-850.

Stewart, R.E.A. and D.M. Lavigne. 1980. Neonatal growth in Northwest Atlantic harp seals, *Pagophilus groenlandicus*. Journal of Mammalogy, 61:670-680.

4. Adaptations for Life in the Sea

Bartholomew, G.A. 1970. A model for the evolution of pinniped polygyny. Evolution, 24:546-559.

Blix, A.S. and J.D. Steen. 1979. Temperature regulation in newborn polar homeotherms. Physiological Reviews, 59:285-304.

Depocas, F., J.S. Hart and H.D. Fisher. 1971. Sea water drinking and water flux in starved and fed harbor seals, *Phoca vitulina*. Canadian Journal of Physiology and Pharmacology, 49:53-62.

Elsner, R. and B. Gooden. 1983. *Diving and asphyxia. A comparative study of animals and man.* Monographs of the Physiological Society. Cambridge University Press, Cambridge, UK.

English, A.W. 1976. Limb movements and locomotor function in the California sea lion (*Zalophus californianus*). Journal of Zoology (London), 178:341-364.

Gentry, R.L. 1981. Seawater drinking in eared seals. Comparative Biochemistry and Physiology, 68A:81-86.

Gentry, R.L. and G.L. Kooyman (eds.). 1986. *Fur seals. Maternal strategies on land and at sea.* Princeton University Press, Princeton, New Jersey.

Gordon, K.R. 1983. Mechanics of the limbs of the walrus (*Odobenus rosmarus*) and the California sea lion (*Zalophus californianus*). Journal of Morphology, 175:73-90.

Innes, S., D.M. Lavigne, W.M. Earle and K.M. Kovacs. 1987. Feeding rates of seals and whales. Journal of Animal Ecology, 56:115-130.

Kooyman, G.L. 1981. *Weddell seal. Consummate diver.* Cambridge University Press, Cambridge, UK.

Kooyman, G.L, M.A. Castellini and R.W. Davis. 1981. Physiology of diving in marine mammals. Annual Review of Physiology, 43:343-356.

Lavigne, D.M. 1982. Pinniped thermoregulation: Comments on the "Effects of cold on the evolution of pinniped breeding systems." Evolution, 36:409-414.

Lavigne, D.M., C.D. Bernholz and K. Ronald. 1977. Functional aspects of pinniped vision. pp. 135-173. *In* R.J. Harrison (ed.). *Functional anatomy of marine mammals. Volume 3.* Academic Press, London, UK.

Lavigne, D.M., S. Innes, G.A.J. Worthy, K.M. Kovacs, O.J. Schmitz and J.P. Hickie. 1986. Metabolic rates of seals and whales. Canadian Journal of Zoology, 64:279-284.

LeBoeuf, B.J., D.P. Costa, A.C. Huntley, G.L. Kooyman and R.W. Davis. 1986. Pattern and depth of dives in northern elephant seals, *Mirounga angustirostris.* Journal of Zoology (London), 208:1-17.

Muizon, Ch. de. 1982. Phocid phylogeny and dispersal. Annals of the South African Museum, 89:175-213.

Nachtigall, P.E. 1986. Vision, audition, and chemoreception in dolphins and other marine mammals. pp. 79-113. *In* R.J. Schusterman, J.A. Thomas and F.G. Wood (eds.). *Dolphin cognition and behaviour: a comparative approach.* Lawrence Erlbaum Associates, Inc., Publishers, Hillsdale, New Jersey.

Oftedal, O.T., D.J. Boness and R.A. Tedman. 1987. The behavior, physiology, and anatomy of lactation in the Pinnipedia. pp. 175-246. *In* H.H. Genoways (ed.). *Current Mammalogy, Volume 1.* Plenum Press, New York.

Repenning, C.A., C.E. Ray and D. Grigorescu. 1979. Pinniped biogeography. pp. 357-369. *In* J. Gray and A.J. Boucot (eds.). *Historical biogeography, plate tectonics and the changing environment.* Oregon State University Press, Corvallis.

Schusterman, R. 1981. Behavioral capabilities of seals and sea lions: A review of their hearing, visual, learning and diving skills. The Psychological Record, 31:125-143.

Stirling, I. 1982. The evolution of mating systems in pinnipeds. pp. 489-527. *In* J.F. Eisenberg and D.G. Kleiman (eds.). *Recent advances in the study of mammalian behavior.* Special Publication of the American Society of Mammalogists. No. 7.

Tarasoff, F.J. 1974. Anatomical adaptations in the river otter, sea otter and harp seal with reference to thermal regulation. pp. 111-141. *In* R.J. Harrison (ed.). *Functional anatomy of marine mammals. Volume 2.* Academic Press, London.

Wartzok, D., R.J. Schusterman and J. Gailey-Phipps. 1984. Seal echolocation? Nature, 308:753.

Zapol, W.M. 1987. Diving adaptations of the Weddell seal. Scientific American, 256(6):100-105.

5. *History of the Northwest Atlantic Seal Hunt*

Boggs, W.S. 1942. *The postage stamps and postal history of Newfoundland.* Chambers Publishing Company, Kalamazoo, Michigan. (Reprinted in 1975 by Quarterman Publications, Inc., Lawrence, Massachusetts. This edition also reproduces: Poole, B.W.H and H.E. Huber. 1922. *Postage stamps of Newfoundland.* Severn-Wylie-Jewett Co., Portland, Maine.)

Brown, C. and H. Horwood. 1974. *Death on the ice. The Great Newfoundland Sealing Disaster of 1914.* Doubleday Canada Limited, Toronto.

Busch, B.C. 1985. *The war against the seals. A history of the North American seal fishery.* McGill-Queen's University Press, Kingston and Montreal.

England, G.A. 1924. *Vikings of the ice. Being the log of a tenderfoot on the Great Newfoundland Seal Hunt.* Doubleday, Page & Company, Garden City, New York. (Reprinted in 1969 as *The greatest hunt in the world.* Tundra Books, Montreal.)

Greene, W.H. 1933. *The wooden walls among the ice floes, Telling the romance of the Newfoundland seal fishery.* Hutchinson & Co. (Publishers) Limited, London.

Lust, P. 1967. *The last seal pup. The story of Canada's seal hunt.* Harvest House Ltd., Montreal.

Mowat, F. 1984. *Sea of slaughter.* McClelland and Stewart Limited, Toronto.

Mowat, F. and D. Blackwood. 1973. *Wake of the great sealers.* McClelland and Stewart Limited, Toronto.

Ryan, S. 1987. *Seals and sealers. A pictorial history of the Newfoundland seal fishery.* Breakwater Books Limited, St. John's, Newfoundland.

Sergeant, D.E. 1976. History and present status of populations of harp and hooded seals. Biological Conservation, 10:95-117.

6. *Future Prospects*

Beddington, J.R., R.J.H. Beverton and D.M. Lavigne (eds.). 1985. *Marine mammals and fisheries.* George Allen & Unwin, London, UK.

Malouf, A. 1986. *Seals and sealing in Canada. Report of the Royal Commission* (Three Volumes). Supply and Services Canada, Ottawa.

Tourist information

For up-to-date information on tours to see harp and hooded seals in the Gulf of St. Lawrence contact:

The International Fund for Animal Welfare, 275 Mill Way, P.O. Box 212, Barnstable, Massachusetts 02630 USA.

Glossary

Aerobic: (see metabolism).

Anaerobic: literally, without air (see metabolism).

Astigmatism: a structural defect in the curvature of the cornea or lens of the eye in which the image of a point projected onto the retina does not appear as a point but rather as a line. As a consequence, indistinct or blurred images are formed.

Autonomic nervous system: that part of the nervous system that innervates most internal organ systems. Unlike the somatic nervous system that innervates muscles that we move at will, the autonomic nervous system ordinarily functions without our awareness.

Beater: a harp seal pup that has moulted its white lanugo; pups are approximately three weeks old when they reach this stage and remain beaters throughout their first year of life.

Bedlamer: a harp seal in spotted pelage, after it has moulted its beater pelt, but before any harp pattern has started to emerge.

Bends: also known as 'decompression sickness' or caisson disease. Pains that often attack a person who goes too quickly from a place of high or low pressure to one of normal pressure as in deep-sea diving or high-altitude flying; caused when gases in the body come out of solution and form bubbles, especially in the joints.

Blueback: a hooded seal pup in neonatal pelage (from birth until its first moult at approximately 14 months of age).

Bradycardia: a drop in heart rate, such as that which occurs when a seal dives. In contrast, an increased heart rate is called tachycardia.

Breeding: (as in 'the breeding season'). This term is used in so many ways that its meaning tends to become obscured. It may be used to refer to the entire process of reproduction or to the various activities that are involved in reproduction, e.g. mating, whelping, nursing and the taking care of offspring.

Brown Fat: a specialized type of fatty tissue frequently found in hibernating mammals and in newborn mammals including humans. Brown fat differs from normal 'white' fat in that it is capable of a high rate of oxygen consumption and, therefore, heat production. It permits hibernating mammals to warm up rapidly after a long winter's sleep and allows newborn mammals to respond quickly to a drop in their deep body temperature. Some species of seals also use brown fat around blood vessels to re-heat cooled blood returning to the heart from the periphery of the animal.

Caisson disease or **caisson sickness:** see the 'bends'.

Carrying capacity: the maximum number of animals belonging to a given species that can be supported permanently in an area.

Cranial: with reference to the cranium or head, e.g. 'cranial sinuses' are sinuses located in the head or skull.

Cusps: the points or bumps on the biting surface of a tooth, e.g. human molars, such as the wisdom teeth, have four cusps.

Estrus: the condition in female mammals when they are sexually receptive, i.e. in 'heat'.

Fat whitecoat: a harp seal pup approximately one week old. Normal pups of this age are pristinely white and extremely fat.

Food web: the complex array of feeding relationships within an ecosystem. When the feeding relationships are simple, e.g. when blue whales eat krill (small shrimp-like animals) that eat phytoplankton (single celled-plants), we often refer to a 'food chain'.

Front: the area of the northwest Atlantic east and north of the island of Newfoundland; one of the locations where harp and hooded seals congregate on ice each year to reproduce.

Gregarious: sociable, fond of the company of others, living in herds or flocks.

Greycoat: a harp seal pup nine to twelve days of age. The darkly coloured juvenile pelage begins to show through the white lanugo giving the pup an overall grey hue. The lanugo also becomes loose during the latter part of this stage.

Gulf: the Gulf of St. Lawrence; one of the locations where harp seals and hooded seals congregate on ice each year to reproduce.

Hakapik: a tool first used by Norwegians to kill young seals; its use is now permitted both on the Front and in the Gulf. The modern *hakapik* has an iron head with a curved spike about 14 centimeters (5 1/2 inches) long on one side and a blunt projection about one centimeter (1/2 inch) on the other, and this head is mounted on a wooden handle up to 1.5 meters (5 feet) long.

Hypermetropia: farsightedness, abnormal vision in which the rays of light are focussed behind the retina. As a result objects appear out of focus. Distant objects are seen more clearly than near ones.

Lactation: the secretion of milk by the mammary gland, a unique feature among mammals; the period during which milk is secreted; and the suckling (or nursing) of young.

Lanugo or **foetal hair:** the covering of fine hair found in most mammals, including humans, while still in the womb or uterus. This foetal hair is usually moulted before birth. For a number of true seals, this lanugo is retained after birth as a well developed pelt. Seals such as the harp seal have white lanugo, giving the pups their common name – 'whitecoat'. Other seals, such as those that live in the Antarctic, have a dark lanugo.

Lead: a channel of open water within the ice-fields.

Metabolism: the molecular tranformations and interactions that provide for an organism's growth and being. That part of metabolism that has to do with the building up of larger molecules from smaller ones is referred to as anabolism. That which has to do with the breaking down of larger molecules into smaller ones is known as catabolism. The latter process releases energy. Metabolism may take place in the presence of oxygen (aerobic metabolism) or in the absence of oxygen (anaerobic metabolism).

Metabolic rate: a measure of the turnover of chemical energy by an organism. In mammals like seals, it can be estimated directly by measuring the amount of heat energy released per unit time or, indirectly, by measuring the amount of oxygen consumed per unit time. By this definition, larger animals have higher metabolic rates (total energy turnover) than do smaller animals. Frequently, however, metabolic rates are expressed on a unit body weight basis (specific metabolic rate). When expressed in this way, specific metabolic rates (energy turnover per unit body weight) of smaller animals are higher than those of larger animals.

Moulting patch: a concentration of harp or hooded seals on the ice for the purpose of shedding their old hair.

Myopia: nearsightedness, an abnormal eye condition in which light rays from distant objects are focussed in front of the retina rather than on it. As a result objects appear out of focus. Near objects are seen more clearly than distant ones.

Newborn or **neonate:** a harp seal pup just after birth, while still wet with birth fluids and marked by birth blood.

Otariid: a member of the pinniped Family Otariidae, i.e. a fur seal or a sea lion – the eared seals.

Pack ice: extensive, free floating areas of local, annually formed ice, occasionally containing multiyear (Arctic) ice.

Pelage: the hairy or furry covering that is found in mammals.

Phocid: a member of the pinniped Family Phocidae, i.e. a hair seal or true seal – the earless seals.

Photoreceptors: cells in the retina of the eye that detect light and initiate nerve impulses to the brain.

Post-natal: after birth.

Pinnipeds: members of the mammalian Order Carnivora known as sea lions, fur seals, walrus and true seals.

Ragged-jacket: a harp seal pup that is approximately two weeks old, that has begun to shed its white lanugo, revealing patches of dark juvenile pelage.

Rapture of the deep: or nitrogen narcosis; a condition similar to being drunk (intoxication) caused by a high concentration of nitrogen in the body.

Refractive index: sometimes referred to as index of refraction or optical density. When a light beam passes at an angle from one substance to another, e.g. from air to water, the light beam changes speed and as a result, it appears to bend. The amount of bending or refraction will depend on the difference between the **refractive indices** of the two substances. The refractive index of a substance is determined by dividing the speed of light in a vacuum by the speed of light passing through the substance. The higher the refractive index of the substance, the slower light is able to travel through it. The speed of light in air is similar to the speed of light in a vacuum and therefore the refractive index of air is nearly 1.00. The refractive index of water is about 1.33.

Sculp: the pelt and attached blubber that are removed together when a seal is skinned or 'sculped'. The remainder of the body is called the carcass or body core.

Sedentary: remaining stationary in one place, fixed to one spot.

Spotted harp: a harp seal that has started to develop the black harp on its back, but still possesses the spots characteristic of bedlamers.

Thermal conductivity: the rate of heat transfer across a sheet of material of unit thickness and unit temperature difference between its surfaces, usually expressed in units of Watts per meter per degree Centigrade ($Wm^{-1}°C^{-1}$); the higher the thermal conductivity of a material, the lower its insulative value. Water has a thermal conductivity more than 20 times that of air. Stationary air has a low thermal conductivity and therefore is an effective insulator.

Thin whitecoat: a harp seal pup that has lost the yellow coloration of the amniotic fluid and now has an overall white colour to the lanugo. Pups of this stage are from three to five days old.

Train oil or **train, trayne oil** or **trayne:** oil derived from sea animals including pinnipeds, whales and seabirds.

True seal: a hair seal or earless seal, a member of the Family Phocidae (see phocid).

Whale: any member of the mammalian Order Cetacea, commonly known as cetaceans; including the toothed whales (porpoises and dolphins, including the beluga or white whale, the narwhal, killer whale (*Orca*), and the sperm whale), Suborder Odontoceti; and the baleen whales (the 'Great' whales, including the blue whale, fin whale, humpback whale, gray whale and right whale), Suborder Mysticeti.

Whelping: the act of giving birth, parturition.

Whelping patch: a concentration of harp or hooded seals formed on the ice for the purpose of giving birth and nursing young. Mating also takes place in the same area.

Whitecoat: a neonatal harp seal before it sheads its white foetal hair or lanugo.

Yellowcoat: a harp seal pup from one to three days old, bearing a yellow stain on its pelage from the amniotic fluids of the womb.

Index

a

Acadians 100, 107, 109
Amundsen, R. 120
Antarctic exploration 119, 120, 126, 132
Antarctic seals 4, 68, 74, 89
anti-sealing movement 133, 135, 136, 137, 140-146,
151, 152, 154
autonomic nervous system 71, 165

b

Bartlett, Captain R. 132
'bends' 56, 73, 77, 78, 165
blubber 22, 26, 34, 38, 41, 47, 59-60, 63, 64, 95,
96, 112
bradycardia 71, 165
Brown C. 121
brown fat 26, 61, 165

c

Caribbean monk seal 2
carrying capacity 157, 165
Chafe, L. 126, 127
club 134-135
cod fishery 104, 106, 112, 114, 115, 154, 156
codworm 154, 156
common seal   see harbour seal
Committee on Seals and Sealing (COSS) 136,
143, 144, 148
culling 152, 154, 155, 156, 157

d

Davies, B. 133, 138
diving 67-78
diving depths 73-77, 82
diving times 67-69, 72, 76
human divers 58, 64, 67, 68, 72, 73, 75
nitrogen 56, 73, 78
northern elephant seal 59, 63, 68, 69, 74, 75,
76, 77
oxygen 67-72, 77
pressure 67, 72, 73, 77, 86
time-depth recorder 73, 74
Weddell seal 68, 69, 70, 74, 76
distribution
modern pinnipeds 6
harp seals 11-16
hooded seals 16-19
Denmark 134, 142, 143
Dundee sealers 115, 117, 125, 127

e

ears 4, 5, also see hearing
eared seals 4, 5, also see otariid seals, Otariidae
earless seals 4, also see phocid seals, Phocidae,
true seals
echolocation 86-87
England, G.A. 104, 132
elephant seals 2, 4, 59, 63, 68, 69, 74, 75-77, 84,
87, 95
European Economic Community 146, 147, 158
European import ban 146, 147, 154, 158
European Parliament 146
evolution 5, 56-57, 67
eye see vision

f

fisheries, interactions with seals 152, 154-157
flippers 2, 4-5 23, 30, 32, 61, 63-67
feeding adaptations 83-91, 95, 96
food requirements of marine mammals 62, 155
Front 12, 13, 16, 115, 117, 132, 134, 135, 140, 145, 166
fur seals 2, 4, 5, 58, 59, 65-67, 69, 76, 87, 88, 95, 96,
also see eared seals, Otariidae, otariid seals

g

gaff 135
Greene, Major W.H. 133
Greenland 7, 14, 15, 16, 19, 99, 115, 117, 121,
142, 143
Greenpeace 140-141
grey seals 69, 76, 87, 101
exploitation 101-102, 109
Gulf of St. Lawrence 11, 12, 13, 15, 16, 84, 100,
101, 103, 109, 110, 124, 129, 130, 132, 134, 135,
137, 138, 142, 145, 148, 151, 155, 158, 166

h

haemoglobin 70
hair 5, 6, 14, 26, 40, 45, 58, 59, 94, 95, 167
foetal hair (lanugo) 27, 28, 39, 40, 45, 166
hakapik 135, 166
harbour seals 68, 69, 76, 87, 101
exploitation 102
harp seal 6-7, 11-16, 21-44, 61, 65, 66, 69, 76, 79,
84, 87-89
beaters 27, 41, 45, 165
birth 13, 16, 21, 23, 25, 37, 45
description 7, 27, 42-44
distribution and migration 11-16, 83

exploitation 97, 103-148
feeding 11, 14, 15, 24, 25, 31, 37, 38, 41, 156
future prospects 154-158
greycoats 27, 34, 166
Jan Mayen population 12, 13, 15
life cycle 21-44, 93
life span 22, 44
mating 13, 34, 37, 95
moulting 14, 15, 16, 39, 41
natural mortality 25, 44
newborns 21, 25, 27, 31, 167
nursing 16, 31, 32, 33, 34, 37, 38, 41, 95
placenta 26
present status 155
quota management 137
ragged-jackets 27, 39, 167
scientific names 6-7
size 7, 22, 25
whelping 13, 21, 26, 35, 37, 40
whitecoats 2, 25, 27, 28, 33, 35, 166, 168
White Sea population 12, 13, 15
yellowcoats 27, 28, 168
hearing 84-86
hooded seal 8-9, 16-19, 45-53, 65, 66, 69, 76, 79, 87, 89
birth 17, 18, 45, 46, 47, 51, 52
bluebacks 45, 47, 52, 165
Davis Strait 'population' 16
description 8-9
distribution and migration 16-19
exploitation 97, 103-148
feeding 16, 19
future prospects 155-158
Jan Mayen 'population' 16
life cycle 45-53, 93
life span 22, 53
mating 47-51, 95
moulting 11, 18, 19, 47, 51, 52
natural mortality 53
nursing 47, 50, 51, 95
placenta 45
present status 155
quota management 140
scientific name 8
size 9, 22, 45
whelping 16, 18, 19, 51

i
Innuit 88, 99, 103, 142, 151
International Commission for the Northwest
    Atlantic Fisheries (ICNAF) 134, 143
International Fund for Animal Welfare (IFAW)
    133, 154

k
Karlsen Shipping Company Ltd. 128, 130
Kean, Captain A. 122-124, 133
Kean, Captain W. 121, 122

l
landsmen 106, 110, 111, 129, 131, 136, 138, 142, 147
locomotion 64-67

m
Magdalen Islands 12, 100-102, 107, 111, 129, 132,
    136, 138, 147, 149
metabolic rate 62, 71, 167
metabolism 58, 69, 70, 166
    aerobic 69, 72, 165
    anaerobic 69, 71, 72, 165
monk seals 2, 4, 59, 87
Moores, The Hon. F.D. 143
myoglobin 70

n
New France 104
Newfoundland 11, 12, 15, 19, 41, 99, 100,
    103-107, 110-140
Northwest Atlantic Fisheries Organization
    (NAFO) 143
Norway 111, 128, 129, 132, 134, 136, 143

o
Odobenidae 4, also see walrus
Otariidae 4, also see eared seals, otariid seals, fur
    seals, sea lions
otariid seals 66, 90, 91, 94, 95, 167, also see eared
    seals, Otariidae, fur seals, sea lions

p
Phocidae 4, also see earless seals, phocid seals,
    true seals
phocid seals 66, 67, 68, 76, 87, 89, 90, 93, 95, 167,
    also see earless seals, Phocidae, true seals
placenta 26, 45, 71
Pimlott, Dr. D. 134
pinnipeds 2-6, 57, 58, 61-68, 70-77, 80, 81, 85-89,
    91-93, 96, 167
    distribution 5, 92
    evolution 5, 56, 67, 78, 82, 84, 88, 92
    living species 3
    reproductive strategies 92-97
polar bears 37, 39, 53
Prince Edward Island 1, 12, 100, 132, 149
pro-sealing movement 138, 143, 144, 151, 152, 154

q
Queen Victoria 114, 121

r

'rapture of the deep' 56, 73, 77, 167
reproductive strategies 92-97
ringed seal 68, 69, 76, 87
Royal Commission on Seals and Sealing 134, 146-148

s

Sable Island 100-102
Scott, Captain R.F. 120, 132
SCUBA 68, 70, 73, 75, 77, 85
sculps 112, 167
sea lions 4, 5, 58, 59, 65-67, 69, 76, 88, 93, 95, 96, also see eared seals, Otariidae, otariid seals
seal oil 6, 100, 101, 102, 104-106, 112, 117, 125, 129, 131, 168
seal hunt 6, 9, 11, 16, 19, 44, 98-148, 151, 152, 154-158
Seal Protection Regulations 133-136
Shackleton, E. 119, 126
Siddon, The Hon. T. 147
Smallwood, J. 130
smell, sense of 83
Spitz, M. 64
S.S. Newfoundland 121-124
S.S. Southern Cross 124
swimming 41, 47, 55, 58, 61, 64-68, 87
St. Pierre et Miquelon 100

t

teeth 5, 30, 88-91, 166
Templeman, Dr. W. 134
Terra Nova 120, 121, 132
thermoregulation 26, 40, 58-64, 92
thermal conductivity 58, 168
tourism 6, 29, 84, 138, 148, 149, 158, 163
true seals 4, 5, 59, 65, 67, 93-95, 97, 168, also see earless seals, Phocidae, phocid seals
tusks 5, 90-91, 96, 100

u

USSR 12, 132

v

vibrissae 87-88
vision 78-84, 166, 167

w

walrus 4-5, 60, 61, 65, 67, 69, 76, 87, 90, 95, 96, also see Odobenidae
exploitation 96, 100, 101, 103, 109
water balance 91-92
Water Street merchants 116, 121
Weddell seals 68, 69, 70, 74, 76, 83
whales 44, 53, 57, 60, 62, 71, 80, 83, 86, 100, 105, 157, 168
Wright brothers 125
World Wars
World War I 124, 125, 128
World War II 111, 120, 125, 128, 129, 131

Photo: R.E.A. Stewart

David M. Lavigne is a Professor in the Department of Zoology, University of Guelph in Guelph, Ontario. He received an Honours B.Sc. from the University of Western Ontario in 1968. After teaching high school for one year, he entered Graduate School at the University of Guelph, receiving an M.Sc. in 1972 and a Ph.D. in 1974, both for work on vision in seals. Although he remained at Guelph, his research interests shifted, first to problems of censusing harp seals to estimate annual pup production and population size. Since 1975, the principal focus of his research has been on the subject of pinniped bioenergetics – the role of seals in the marine food web. While at Guelph, David has taught numerous courses, including mammalogy, several courses in ecology and marine biology, and a graduate course in marine mammal ecology. The author of numerous publications on various aspects of seal biology, he is also co-editor (with J. Beddington and R.J.H. Beverton) of the book *Marine Mammals and Fisheries*, published by George Allen & Unwin in 1985. He is currently writing a book entitled: *The Pinnipeds: A Functional Approach*.

Kit M. Kovacs is an Assistant Professor in the Department of Biology, University of Waterloo in Waterloo, Ontario. She was first exposed to pinnipeds, working as a research technician studying walruses, while completing an Honours B.Sc. at York University. She then pursued an interest in the evolution of vertebrate mating systems, studying the peculiar situation where pairs of female ring-billed gulls tend nests and raise a common brood, earning an M.Sc. from Lakehead University in 1982. Supported by a Postgraduate Scholarship from the Natural Sciences and Engineering Research Council of Canada, Kit conducted research on harp seals in eastern Canada and grey seals in the United Kingdom between 1982 and 1986, concentrating on the interactions between mothers and their pups. For this work, she was awarded a Ph.D. from the University of Guelph in 1986. Returning to the United Kingdom as an NSERC Post-doctoral fellow at Cambridge, she studied common (harbour) seals on the Orkney Islands in the north of Scotland, in association with the Sea Mammal Research Unit in Cambridge. In her current position, she is continuing her research on seals and teaching courses in ecology, population biology and animal behaviour. Professors Kovacs and Lavigne also teach a field course entitled 'The Biology of Marine Mammals' at the Huntsman Marine Laboratory in St. Andrews, New Brunswick.

Postscript

On Wednesday, 30 December 1987, after *Harps & Hoods* had gone to the printer, The Minister of Fisheries and Oceans, The Hon. Tom Siddon, announced the 'implementation of key recommendations of the Royal Commission on Seals and Sealing' and a 'new seal policy' for Canada.

'Under the new seal policy, the government will no longer permit the large vessel offshore seal hunt in Canadian waters. All commercial hunting of whitecoat harp seals and blueback hooded seals will be ended.'

Despite headlines in the Canadian press the following day, Mr. Siddon's announcement does not mean the end of the seal hunt off eastern Canada. As his press release stated:

> ... the annual harvest of older seals by Inuit and other coastal people will continue. New Seal Protection Regulations, covering all seals in Canadian waters, will ensure that the harvest is conducted as humanely as possible and in accordance with the principles of the World Conservation Strategy and the guidelines outlined by the Royal Commission. The netting of seals will be phased out over five years except for traditional hunts north of 53 degrees north latitude.
>
> The government will continue to work with the Inuit Tapirisat of Canada and the Canadian Sealers Association to ensure sound harvesting practices and to utilize the earlier authorized $5 million funding to develop new opportunities for the sealers and sealing communities that were affected by the collapse of the sealing industry.

The 'new seal policy' essentially formalizes changes in the way the seal hunt has been conducted since the imposition of the European import ban in 1983. Although large vessels will no longer be allowed to go sealing and whitecoats and bluebacks will no longer be killed, harp seal pups can still be taken by landsmen sealers when their white coats have begun to moult (ragged-jackets) and after their first moult is completed (beaters). The hunt for older animals, immature bedlamers and adults, is not affected by the new policy.

As a consequence of the new policy, Canada's seal hunt will now be restricted to landsmen, largely from Newfoundland, the Magdalen Islands and the North Shore of the St.

Lawrence River, and to aboriginal peoples farther north. Between 1974 and 1983, the annual landsmen catch ranged from 40,000 to 110,000 harp seals and averaged almost 68,000 seals per year. In 1987, it still exceeded 40,000 animals.

No quotas for future seal hunts were announced but the references to the *World Conservation Strategy* (WCS) and the guidelines of the Royal Commission may provide some insights into the intention of the new sealing policy. One of the three main objectives of the WCS (prepared by the International Union for Conservation of Nature and Natural Resources (IUCN), in collaboration with the United Nations Environment Programme (UNEP), and the World Wildlife Fund (WWF), and published in March 1980) is:

> to ensure the sustainable utilisation of species and ecosystems (notably fish and other wildlife, forests and grazing lands), which support millions of rural communities as well as major industries.

The Royal Commission Report, in recommending that the whitecoat hunt should not be allowed in the future, noted that:

> There appears to be less opposition to the killing of older seals and some sympathy for the people in the small isolated communities in northern Newfoundland and elsewhere.

It also recommended that the possibility of a cull (as opposed to a hunt) of harp seals at some time in the future 'might be seriously considered' and did not rule out the possibility of killing seal pups (e.g. whitecoats) on breeding grounds 'as a measure of population control'.

Canada's new sealing policy thus maintains the flexibility to revitalize the seal hunt in the years to come, should market conditions improve, or to replace the hunt with a government-controlled cull.

The story of *Harps & Hoods* continues ...

D.M.L. & K.M.K.
2 January 1988